PSYCHOLOGY
and
SOCIAL SCIENCES
for
MRCPsych

Tanvir Ahmad Rana DPM, MRCPsych.
Specialist Registrar
Birmingham & Solihull Mental NHS Trust

Shabbir Ahmad Rana Mphil
School of Psychology
Leicester University

PEDRO PRESS PUBLICATIONS

Published by: **Pedro Press Publications**

23 Blakey Street

Manchester

M12 5QF

UK

ISBN

0-9550873-0-9

A catalogue record for this title is available from the British Library

Printed and bound in Malaysia by T. Associates

To

Wazir Ahmad Rana and Rahmat Begum,
our parents,

for providing us wonderful educational opportunities

CONTENTS

ACKNOWLEDGEMENTS

This book would not have been possible without the contribution and assistance of following people. They motivated and helped us in various ways and we want to express our heartfelt thanks and gratitude.

Prof. I A.K.Tareen, Prof.Khalida I. Tareen,
Dr. M.A. Zahid Bajwa, Ch. Ali Asghar,
Dr. Maqsood Ahmad, Dr. Khalid Saeed,
Dr. Anjum Bashir, Dr. Ayesha Tareen,
Dr. Arshad Mahmood, Dr. J.N.M. Kennedy,
Dr. A. Jawad Sheikh, Dr. Azhar Ali Rizwi,
Prof. Saleem Shiekh, Dr. Ruhi Khalid,
Dr. Kausar Sohail, Dr. Sh. Asif Zia,
Prof. Rukhsana Kausar, Ch. Baber Shafi,
Dr. Tahir Suleman, Dr. Bhawna Chowda
and Mian Abbas Ali.

We would like to acknowledge the dept we owe to the authors & publishers of the books name in the reference list. On a more personal level, we would also like to express our deepest appreciation for Amera and Saima, our wives, for their endless support and sustenance.

TAR

SAR

INTRODUCTION

Psychology and social sciences are important and substantial components of MRCPsych theory examinations. In spite of numerous textbooks on these subjects most doctors still find it very daunting to attempt the MCQs (now called ISQs). This book was conceived in response to this difficulty. As far as we are aware this is the first book in UK comprising of ISQs solely on psychology and social sciences. Although this book is primarily aimed at the doctors appearing for both part - I and part- II of MRCPsych examination, it would hopefully be useful for other postgraduate examinations in psychiatry as well as psychology .
As we are acutely aware that the ISQs can be framed in many possible ways , we have deliberately strived to impart crucial and core information as clearly as possible rather than utilizing terms such as commonly, often, and frequently etc. We believe the candidates would be familiar with their implications.

As there is considerable overlap between various topics of psychology, some questions could appropriately be grouped under other topics rather than the way they have been classified in this book. Needless to say the more important thing is to become familiar with and learn as many ISQs as possible.

A reference list of the books is provided. We found these books very helpful and would recommend them for further reading.

Any constructive criticism and comments would be greatly appreciated and can be sent at: tanvirrana786@hotmail.com

Good luck!

Tanvir Ahmad Rana
Shabbir Ahmad Rana
14^{tth} August, 2005

1

1. HUMAN GROWTH & DEVELOPMENT

1. Bonding is infant to mother.
2. Imprinting occurs in primates.
3. Thomas and Chess described six aspects of temperaments.
4. According to Piaget, Schema refers to the incorporation of new information.
5. According to Piaget, Assimilation refers to cognitive structure or pattern of behaviour.
6. According to Piaget, Assimilation refers to the adjustment of existing schemas so as to facilitate comprehension of new information.
7. Sensorimotor stage is from 0-4 years.
8. Pre-operational stage is from 2-7 years.
9. Pre-operational stage has object permanence and animism.
10. Sensorimotor stage has precausal logic.
11. According to Piaget's theory of cognitive development, animism means that characteristics of life are attributed to all objects.
12. According to Piaget, the concrete operational stage occurs from 7-14 years.
13. Formal operational stage is from 11 years onwards.
14. According to Kohlberg's theory of moral development, there are six stages and three levels of moral development.
15. According to Kohlberg's theory of moral development, level I have stage of approval and disapproval.
16. According to Kohlberg's theory of moral development, level-I has stages of punishment and reward.
17. According to Kohlberg's theory of moral development, post-

conventional morality is at level III.

18. Sexual identity refers to biological status as male/female.

19. Gender identity is a person's self-awareness as male/female.

20. According to Ramsay and de Groot, there are three phases of grief work.

21. According to Kubler Ross, terminally ill people use anticipatory grief to come to terms with their imminent death.

22. According to Bowlby, new-born human are entirely helpless and are under genetic control to behave towards their mother in specific ways in order to ensure their survival.

23. According to Thomas and Chess, the nine categories of temperament of children can be clustered in three types: easy child, difficult child, and very difficult child.

24. According to Piaget's theory of cognitive development, circular reaction occurs in sensorimotor stage.

25. According to Piaget's theory of cognitive development, secondary circular reactions occur from two to five months and have no apparent purpose.

26. According to Piaget's theory of cognitive development, tertiary circular reactions occur from five to nine months.

27. According to Piaget's theory of cognitive development, object permanence is fully developed at one year.

28. According to Piaget's theory of cognitive development, egocentrism occurs in sensorimotor stage.

29. According to Piaget's theory of cognitive development, animism occurs in sensorimotor stage.

30. According to Piaget's theory of cognitive development, artificialism means that life, thoughts and feelings are attributed to all objects, including inanimate ones.

31. According to Piaget's theory of cognitive development, egocentrism occurs in both sensorimotor as well as preoperational stage.

32. According to Piaget's theory of cognitive development, precausal reasoning occurs in concrete operational stage. reasoning occurs in concrete operational stage.

33. According to Piaget's theory of cognitive development, laws of conservation occur in concrete operational stage.

34. According to Piaget's theory of cognitive development, the formal operational stage occurs from 16 years.

35. Kohlberg's theory of moral development consists of six development stages.

36. According to Kohlberg's theory of moral development, in stage three rules are adhered to so as to avoid the disapproval of others.

37. According to Kohlberg's theory of moral development, conventional morality occurs at level III.

38. Most children acquire a permanent gender identity by the age of four.

39. According to Social Disengagement Theory of old age; the healthy, older adult actively disengages from roles and relationships.

40. According to Peck, coming to terms with our own deaths, is a state called ego-transcendence versus ego-preoccupation.

41. According to Piaget, cognitive abilities undergo a smooth progression through childhood.

42. According to Piaget, development of cognition consists of a progression from subjective conception to the objective.

43. According to Piaget's sensorimotor stage, an infant is unable to conceive of an object's existence when it is no longer in the visual field.

44. Piaget's sensorimotor stage spans from birth to 2 years.

45. According to Piaget, when children are nearly two years old,

they are able to conceptualise hidden objects.

46. According to Piaget's preoperational stage, a child fails to recognise conservation of different quantities.

47. According to Piaget's concrete operational stage, a child's reasoning is illogical.

48. Piaget's preoperational stage lasts from two to eight years of age.

49. According to Piaget's preoperational stage, a child is able to distinguish between self and not self.

50. According to Piaget's preoperational stage, a child is unable to appreciate the fact that one's view of reality is but one of many possible views.

51. According to Piaget's theory of cognitive development, the phenomenon of non-conservation occurs in preoperational stage.

52. According to Piaget's theory, in preoperational stage a child has the ability of class inclusion.

53. According to Piaget, a child is egocentric in the preoperational stage.

54. According to Piaget, a newborn has in built repertoire of reflexes called motor schemes.

55. According to Piaget, motor schemes provide the foundations for subsequent cognitive feats.

56. According to Piaget's theory of cognitive development, the processes of assimilation and accommodation work in a complementary way.

57. Equilibrium is one of Piaget's concepts.

58. Piaget's theory of cognitive development has been strongly challenged by other researchers.

59. Most researchers disagree with Piaget that cognitive development is not a continuous process.

60. According to theory of mind, a child hypothesises about a

person's unseen mental constructs and is able to predict the behaviour of the person.

61. According to Frith, autism is due to deficiency of a theory of mind.

62. Imprinting is a form of immediate and irreversible learning.

63. According to Klaus and Kennel, bonding can only occur in the hours following child birth.

64. In neonates, adult's levels of visual acuity are not attained until the age of six months.

65. Neonates show preference for mother's face and voice.

66. Neonates show an innate preference for sweet tastes.

67. In neonates, the smile starts becoming discriminating from six months onwards.

68. At six months, the infant is aware that certain behaviour can elicit pleasurable responses in others.

69. At eight months the infant can recognise the caregiver and will become distressed at his or her departure.

70. At eight months, the infant understands the concept of object permanence.

71. Attachment figures can be other children.

72. Piaget's preoperational stage includes mastery of conservation.

73. Piaget's preoperational stage includes animism.

74. In monkeys, normal development seems to depend on factors other than food.

75. According to Lorenz, imprinting cannot take place without feeding.

76. According to Lorenz, critical period is under genetic control.

77. According to Piaget, children develop the concept of 'reversibility' during pre-operational stage.

78. According to Kohlberg, children first develop consistent gender identity and therefore subsequently attend to the same sex models.

79. Marcia described six statuses of identity development.

80. Crying plays a part in reinforcing attachment.

81. Developmental language delay is one of the effects of maternal deprivation.

82. Enuresis is one of the recognized effects of maternal deprivation.

83. The conventional morality in Kohlberg's moral development theory has two stages.

84. Larger family size is associated with slower speech development.

85. Gender identity is usually established at 3-4 years of age.

86. In old age there may be less challenge to use fluid intelligence.

87. The positive view about aging is based on the decrement model.

88. Older people recover sooner under stressful conditions because of experience and subsequent immunity.

89. As compared to younger people, in older people nerve impulses travel more slowly to the brain but quickly from the brain.

90. In older people, fluid intelligence continues to increase.

91. According to Social Disengagement Theory (Cumming and Henry), there is a systematic
reduction in certain kinds of social interaction so that society renews itself and the elderly are free to die.

92. Regarding memory, tests of recognition demonstrate a significant difference between young and old people.

93. Shrinkage of life space (one aspect of Social Disengagement Theory) means that elderly people are less governed by strict rules and expectations in the few roles that remain for them.

94. Re-Engagement Theory emphasizes that older people are the same as middle-aged people, with essentially the same psychological and social needs.

5. There is universal acceptance of Social Engagement Theory.

6. Erikson's Psychosocial Theory states that old age involves conflict between ego-integrity and Despair.

7. Senescence refers to the period when the degenerative processes of aging set in.

8. Peck's theory states that continued psychological growth during old age depends upon how well individuals cope with two major developmental tasks (vocational retirement and physical decline).

9. Activity theory of aging has significant empirical support.

00. Cavanagh has proposed four stages of bereavement.

01. Atchley has proposed seven phases of retirement.

02. Kubler-Ross identified four stages which the dying person passes through.

03. Bowlby identified seven stages of bereavement.

04. There is strong evidence that bereavement can produce changes in nervous, hormonal and respiratory systems.

05. Functional ways of coping with grief include good communication, acceptance of support, idolization, and absence of guilt.

06. The term ageism implies prejudice towards older people.

07. The term Gender stereotype implies excessively rigid beliefs about what males and females are like and how should they behave?

08. Gender role means the perception of oneself as masculine or feminine.

09. The term androgynous is used to describe people who possess both masculine and feminine characteristics

10. Research indicates that that androgynous individuals are less psychologically healthy and well-adjusted than are

Individuals who are rigidly typed as either masculine or feminine.

111. Gender differences can be observed as early as two to three years of age.

112. Males and females can produce the same range of hormones.

113. Many studies indicate that females exposed to male hormones before birth often later exhibit more masculine gender-role behaviour than matched control group of girls who are not exposed to the harmone.

114. Regarding gender development, Money and Erhardt have argued that in some cases social learning can override biological processes.

115. Studies of individuals who have been born with genetic abnormality (e.g. hermaphroditism) suggests that the effects of socialization on gender development are very powerful.

116. According to Freud, successful resolution during the phallic phase results in child identifying with the same-sex parent.

117. According to Cognitive-developmental theory, the child's growing cognitive abilities lie at the heart of gender role development.

118. Kohlberg's proposal of gender constancy being of central influence in the development of gender role, has received little support.

119. Nearly half of marriages in Western countries end in divorce.

120. Research has shown that marriages of children of divorced parents are more likely to end in divorce as compared to those whose parents do not divorce.

121. Twenty five percent of divorced mothers and 50 percent of divorced fathers will remarry.

122. Research shows that a parental death has a substantially weaker effect on children's psychopathology as compared to marital conflicts and divorce.

123. Research regarding children's play has revealed that 4-6 year old boys and girls are equally likely to play in dyads.

124. Piaget contended that children's developmental level may be totally inferred from their play.

125. Research regarding children's play show that boys are more likely to play with each peer for a longer period of time as compared to girls.

126. Piaget proposed three broad stages of play activity.

127. Vygotsky proposed that socially there is a clear developmental sequence in a child's style of play.

128. Piaget believed that play creates a 'zone of potential development' where children can operate at a level which is above that for their normal age.

129. Parten suggested three developmental sequences in a child's style of play.

130. According to Vygotsky, one way of assessing a child's potential development at a particular time is to note the distance between the levels of activity reached during play and those of his or her customary behaviour.

131. Parten proposed that a three year old child engages in social play.

132. Subsequent studies have not confirmed Parten's developmental sequences of children's play.

133. Bruner has stressed the learning potential of play.

134. The social learning theory of play states that children use play to explore and cope with their feelings about life and work out their fears and anxieties in a safe situation.

135. Sylva et al.'s study of the play of preschool children has important implications for the organization and staffing of nursery schools and playgroups.

136. Physical and sexual abuse are major antecedents of borderline personality disorder.

137. Children who witness domestic violence are vulnerable to emotional and developmental Problems.

138. There is a small association between substance abuse and domestic violence.

139. Regarding domestic violence, Type I husbands are characterized as having an increased heart rate and autonomic reactivity making their violence more impulsive.

140. Self esteem is totally influenced by the reactions of others and comparisons with others.

1. HUMAN GROWTH AND DEVELOPMENT
ANSWERS

1. True.
2. False.
3. False. Nine.
4. False. This is assimilation.
5. False. This is schema.
6. False. This is accommodation.
7. False. 0-2 years.
8. True.
9. False. Object permanence occurs in sensorimotor stage.
10. False. It occurs in pre-operational stage.
11. True.
12. False. From 7-11 years.
13. True.
14. True.
15. False. Level 11 has this stage.
16. True.
17. True.
18. True.
19. True.
20. False. They identified nine components of grief, some occurring early and some late. They are, shock, disorganisation, denial, depression, guilt, anxiety, aggression, resolution and reintegration.
21. True.
22. True.
23. False. The third cluster is slow-to-warm- up child.

24. True.
25. False. These are primary circular reactions.
26. False. These are secondary circular reactions.
27. False. Eighteen months.
28. True.
29. False. In pre-operational stage.
30. False. This is animism.
31. True.
32. False. Pre-operational stage.
33. True.
34. False. 12-14 years onwards.
35. True.
36. True.
37. False. Level 11.
38. False. Although most children have some knowledge about their gender at 3 or 4 years, they have permanent gender identity at 5 years.
39. True. This is one of them.
40. True.
41. False. Progression is in stages.
42. True.
43. True.
44. True.
45. True.
46. True.
47. False. Logical reasoning.
48. False. 2-7 years.
49. True.
50. True

51. True.
52. False. A child lacks this.
53. True.
54. True.
55. True.
56. True.
57. True.
58. True.
59. False. There is a general agreement with this idea.
60. True.
61. True.
62. True.
63. True.
64. True.
65. True.
66. True.
67. False. From three months onwards.
68. True.
69. True.
70. True.
71. True.
72. False.
73. True.
74. True.
75. False. Imprinting occurs through mere exposure without feeding.
76. True.
77. This concept develops in concrete operational stage
78. True.
79. There are four stages, identity achievement, foreclosure,

moratorium and identity diffusion.

80. True.

81. True.

82. True.

83. True.

84. True.

85. True.

86. True.

87. False. This is a negative view of aging which considers aging as a process of decay or decline.

88. False. They recover slowly since the immune system functions less effectively.

89. False. Nerve impulses travel slowly both ways.

90. False. It is cystallized intelligence which continues to increase. Fluid intelligence refers to the ability to solve novel and unusual problems. Crystallized intelligence results from accumulated knowledge.

91. True.

92. False. Very little difference.

93. False. Increased individuality means this. Shrinkage of life space means that older people interact less and occupy less roles.

94. True.

95. False.

96. True.

97. True.

98. False. Third important aspect to final adjustment is related to human morality.

99. False. Very little empirical support has been criticized as an over-simplification.

100. False. Seven stages. Shock, disorganization, violent emotions, guilt, loneliness and loss, relief and reestablishment.

101. True. Remote phase, near preretirement phase, honeymoon phase, disenchantment phase, reorientation phase, stability phase and the terminal phase.

102. False. Five stages. Denial, Anger, Bargaining, Depression and Acceptance.

103. False. Five stages. (a).Concentration on the deceased person,(b). anger toward the deceased or other people, (c). appeals to others for help, (d). despair, withdrawal, disorganization, and (e). reorganization and focus on a new object of interest.

104. True.

105. False. According to Criosby and Jose, idolization is a dysfunctional way.

106. True.

107. True.

108. False. It is gender identity. Gender role means the behaviour, attitudes and activities that are considered by a particular society to be appropriate for males and females.

109. True.

110. False. They are more healthy.

111. True.

112. True.

113. True.

114. False. They have asserted that this occurs in most cases.

115. True.

116. True. During phallic phase child encounters the Oedipus /Electra complex.

117. True.

118. False. There is lot of empirical support.

119. True.

120. True.

121. False. 75 percent of divorced mothers and 80 percent of divorced fathers remarry.

122. True.

123. True.

124. False. Can be inferred in part from their play.

125. False. It's the other way round. Boys have more different partners perhaps because girls have longer attention spans.

126. True. Mastery plays, symbolic play, and play with rules.

127. False. This was proposed by Parten.

128. False. This is Vygotsky's view.

129. True. Solitary play, parallel play and social play.

130. True.

131. False. At four years of age. At three years the child engages in parallel play and does not truly engage with other children.

132. False. Lot of research supports his proposal.

133. True.

134. False. This is psychodynamic view of children's play.

135. True.

136. True.

137. True.

138. False. 50 to 90 percent of batterers have a history of substance abuse.

139. False. Type II husbands. Type I husbands are characterized by a decreased heart rate and autonomic reactivity as the abuse proceeds making their violence more deliberate.

140. False. Partially influenced.

●———————————————●

2. LEARNING AND CONDITIONING

1. Habituation is a simple form of learning.
2. In Classical conditioning new behaviour cannot be learned.
3. Conscious information processing requires attention.
4. In Classical conditioning "higher order" learning means that a previously unconditioned stimulus may be used as an conditioned stimulus.
5. In classical conditioning there is no stimulus generation.
6. In classical conditioning a neutral stimulus is referred to as a conditioned stimulus when it elicits a response.
7. Operant conditioning mainly involves involuntary behaviour.
8. In Operant conditioning consequences determine behaviour.
9. Modelling is an example of operant conditioning.
10. Operant conditioning is ineffective in the modification of automatic responses.
11. The acquisition of phobias usually occurs after a series of traumatic events.
12. Systemic desensitization is effective for obsessive compulsive neurosis.
13. In social learning theory emphasis is laid on conformity to social norms.
14. Habituation is a simple way of learning new behaviour.
15. In Classical conditioning, subjects are active.
16. Delayed conditioning is optimal when the delay between two stimuli is about 0.5 seconds.
17. Simultaneous conditioning is superior to delayed

conditioning.

18. In trace conditioning the conditioned stimulus terminates before onset of the unconditioned stimulus.

19. Operant conditioning is independent of stimulus.

20. In Operant conditioning, discrimination can occur.

21. In Operant conditioning, punishment is a type of negative reinforcement.

22. Biofeedback is an application of classical conditioning.

23. Intermittent reinforcement in operant conditioning leads to greater resistance to extinction than continuous reinforcement.

24. Negative reinforcement is synonymous as punishment.

25. Extinction is   process of gradual disappearance of a conditioned response on discontinuation of an unconditioned stimulus.

26. Classical conditioning takes place irrespective of the schedule of reinforcement.

27. Classical conditioning takes place irrespective of the nature of the unconditioned stimulus.

28. In operant conditioning, variable ratio reinforcement is the easiest to extinguish.

29. Negative reinforcement means reinforcement through withdrawal of unpleasant conditions.

30. Intermittent reinforcement takes the longest to establish.

31. A response is much harder to extinguish if it was acquired during continuous rather than partial reinforcement.

32. Extinction tends to occur with non-reinforcement of a conditioned response.

33. Extinction tends to occur with the repetition of the conditioned stimulus in the absence of the unconditioned stimulus.

34. Associative learning includes classical and operant learning.

35. Observational learning is also known as vicarious learning.

36. Classical learning and respondent learning are synonymous.

37. In classical conditioning the association between unconditioned stimulus and unconditioned response in response to a conditioned stimulus does not require understanding.

38. The period of association between unconditioned stimulus and unconditioned stimulus is called the acquisition stage.

39. Higher order conditioning means that a new conditioned stimulus is learned through association with the original conditioned stimulus.

40. Simultaneous conditioning is more effective than the delayed conditioning.

41. In classical conditioning, trace conditioning is least effective.

42. Generalization is a term used in operant conditioning.

43. Operant behaviour is independent of stimuli.

44. Respondent behaviour is the consequence of known stimuli.

45. In Operant conditioning, primary reinforcement is independent of prior learning.

46. In Operant conditioning, secondary reinforcement is based on prior learning.

47. Aversive conditioning when performed in the imagination is called Covert sensitization.

48. Premack's principle states that high frequency behaviour can be used to reinforce low frequency behaviour.

49. Chaining is a technique used in classical conditioning.

50. In delayed conditioning the onset of the conditioned stimulus precedes that of the unconditioned stimulus and the conditioned stimulus continues until the response occurs.

51. Simultaneous conditioning is less successful than delayed conditioning.

52. Delayed conditioning is optimal when the delay between the onsets of the two stimuli is around one second.

53. The acquisition stage of conditioning is the period during which the association is being acquired between the conditioned stimulus and the conditioned response.

54. In trace conditioning the conditioned stimulus ends after the onset of the unconditioned stimulus.

55. Extinction is the sudden disappearance of a conditioned response.

56. Extinction occurs when the conditioned response is repeatedly presented without the unconditioned stimulus.

57. In Classical conditioning, partial recovery means that a weaker response re-emerges.

58. In Classical conditioning, incubation is the decrease in strength of conditioned responses resulting from repeated brief exposure to the conditioned stimulus.

59. In Classical conditioning, preparedness means that some responses are more likely to become conditioned.

60. In Classical conditioning, generalization means that a response can also be evoked by other stimuli that are similar to the original conditioned stimulus.

61. Thorndike's law of effect states that involuntary behaviour that is paired with subsequent reward is strengthened.

62. Extinction and discrimination occur in both classical as well as operant conditioning.

63. Escape conditioning is a type of negative reinforcement in which the response learnt provides complete escape from the aversive stimulus.

64. In operant conditioning, secondary reinforcement is that driving from association with primary reinforcers.

65. In operant conditioning, continuous reinforcement has maximum response rate.

66. In operant conditioning, variable ratio is very good at maintaining a high response rate.

67. Reciprocal inhibition means that relaxation inhibits anxiety so that the two are mutually exclusive.

68. In the treatment of obsessive compulsive disorder, habituation is used.

69. The basic principle of classical conditioning is that making reinforcement contingent upon a response increases the rate of emission of that response.

70. The conditions under which stimulus-stimulus associations in classical conditioning and action-outcome associations in instrumental conditioning are acquired are different.

71. Regarding learning, as two events become less temporally contiguous, the resultant behaviour from pairing these events become more pronounced.

72. Regarding learning, as one event becomes poorer predictor of a second, the resultant behaviour that results from pairings of these events becomes more pronounced.

73. Research suggests that contiguity alone is sufficient to produce conditioning.

74. Implosion therapy, flooding and systematic desensitisation are used in extinction procedures.

75. Extinction of an unconditioned phobic response may be achieved by sustained and repeated exposure to the phobic object.

76. The phenomenon of blocking (in learning) occurs when a previously established relationship between one stimulus and the unconditioned stimulus prevents the formation of an association between a novel stimulus and the unconditioned stimulus.

77. Extinction occurs when reinforcement is no longer obtained as a result of emitting the response and the level of responding declines.

78. Regarding schedules of reinforcement, when a reward is made dependent upon the emission of a number of responses, it is called interval schedule.

79. Regarding schedules of reinforcement, when a reward is made contingent upon a response being emitted after a period of time, it is called interval schedule.

80. Associative learning in young children is typical of that observed in animals.

81. A schedule of reinforcement is a procedure which allows a reward to be made contingent upon a response.

82. Associative learning in young children and adults is same.

83. Associative learning in young children and animals is the same.

84. Regarding associative learning, the transition between typical animal and adult performance occurs around the age of seven.

85. Language has a limited role to play in instrumental learning.

86. Stimulus generalization is when a response learnt in one situation is exhibited in another.

87. Stimulus discrimination is when a learner responds differently to two slightly different stimuli.

88. Systemic desensitization is a form of operant conditioning.

89. Systemic desensitization is the treatment of choice for obsessional thoughts.

90. Variable ratio schedules of reinforcement can only be used in operant conditioning situations.

91. Variable ratio schedules of reinforcement increases the resistance to extinction.

92. In Classical conditioning spontaneous recovery only occurs after a short delay.

93. In Classical conditioning forward conditioning is when the CS always precedes the UCS.

94. In Classical conditioning the strength of CR is proportional to the intensity of the UCS.

95. Classical conditioning underlies systemic desensitization.

96. Regarding Classical conditioning, second-order conditioning may be a model for the acquisition of phobias.

97. Regarding Classical conditioning, incubation means that some stimuli are more likely to become CS than others.

98. Operant conditioning is the same as instrumental conditioning.

99. In Operant conditioning, extinction and spontaneous do not occur.

100. Escape conditioning is an example of negative conditioning.

101. Behaviour learned through avoidance conditioning is resistant to extinction as it often reinforced by fear reduction.

102. In reinforcement, variable ratio schedule means that reinforcement is given after a variable amount of time.

103. In reinforcement gambling is an example of variable-interval conditioning.

104. In reinforcement behaviour learned through partial reinforcement is very resistant to extinction.

105. Regarding Operant conditioning, shaping is best used when the complete response desired is simple.

106. In incubation, brief and repeated exposures to a stimulus results in strengthening the conditioned response.

107. Vicarious learning and observational learning are synonymous terms.

108. Respondent learning and operant conditioning are synonymous terms.

109. Escape conditioning is a type of aversive conditioning.

110. Negative reinforcement is not the same thing as punishment.

111. Regarding vicarious learning, reinforcement is one of the optimal conditions.

112. Variable-interval schedule is a reinforcement in which a reward is given after a varying number of responses have been emitted.

113. Partial reinforcement is a schedule of reinforcement in which rewards are not given each time a response is made, rendering a learned response highly resistant to extinction.

114. Covert reinforcement is a method of reducing behavioural frequency by using the imagination of unpleasant events as a reinforcement.

115. Variable interval schedule is a reinforcement schedule in which a reward is given after varying periods of time have passed.

116. Negative practice is a method of reducing the frequency of behaviour by intense avoiding of the response.

117. Evidence for reciprocal influences on behaviour is shown by family studies which suggest that pre-delinquent behaviour patterns are set in motion by the excessive and inconsistent use of punishment on the parts of parents.

118. Covert reinforcement is a method of increasing behavioural frequency by using the imagination of pleasant events as a reinforcement.

119. As with classical conditioning, temporal contiguity is essential for learning to occur operant conditioning.

120. The neural mechanism underlying the delayed effect of reinforcement is located in the anterior cingulated cortex.

2. LEARNING AND CONDITIONING
ANSWERS

1.   True.
2.   False.
3.   True.
4.   False. Previously CS may be used as an UCS.
5.   False.
6.   True.
7.   False. Voluntary behaviour.
8.   True.
9.   False.
10.   False.
11.   False.
12.   False.
13.   False.
14.   True.
15.   False.
16.   True.
17.   False. Delayed conditioning is superior.
18.   True.
19.   True.
20.   True.
21.   False.
22.   False. Operant conditioning.
23.   True.
24.   False.
25.   True.
26.   False.

27. False.

28. False.

29. True.

30. True.

31. False. Partial conditioning is difficult to distinguish.

32. True.

33. True.

34. True.

35. True.

36. True.

37. True. It is automatic.

38. False. Conditioned stimulus.

39. True.

40. False. Less effective.

41. True.

42. False. Classical Conditioning.

43. True.

44. True.

45. True.

46. True.

47. True.

48. True.

49. False. Operant conditioning.

50. True.

51. True.

52. False. Half a second.

53. False. Conditioned stimulus and unconditioned stimulus.

54. False. The CS ends before the onset of UCS.

55. False. Gradual disappearance.

56. True.

57. True.

58. False. Increase in strength.

59. False. Stimuli rather than responses.

60. True.

61. False. Voluntary behaviour.

62. True.

63. True.

64. True.

65. True.

66. True.

67. True.

68. True.

69. False.

70. False. They are ought to be similar.

71. False. Less pronounced.

72. False. Less pronounced.

73. False. Contingency is essential.

74. True.

75. False. Conditioned phobic response.

76. True.

77. True.

78. False. Ratio schedule.

79. True.

80. True.

81. True.

82. False. It is different.

83. True.

84. False. Around the age of four or five when children develop a functioning linguistic capacity.

85. False. Important role.

86. False.

87. True.

88. False.

89. False.

90. False.

91. True.

92. False.

93. True.

94. True.

95. True.

96. True.

97. False.

98. True.

99. False.

100. True.

101. True.

102. False.

103. True.

104. True.

105. False.

106. True.

107. True.

108. False. Respondent learning is another name for classical conditioning. Operant conditioning is also known as Instrumental learning.

109. True.

110. True. In operant conditioning, negative reinforcement means that by removing negative reinforcer, response is reinforced.

111. True.

112. False. This is variable-ratio schedule.

113. True
114. False. This is called covert sensitization.
115. True.
116. False. By intense repetition of the response.
117. True.
118. True.
119. False. In both types of conditioning temporal contiguity is not necessary.
120. True

3. LANGUAGE AND THOUGHT

1. Regarding language, phenomes have no meaning in themselves.

2. Regarding language, morphemes are basic units of meaning and consist mainly of words.

3. Syntax refers to the rules for combining words into phrases and sentences.

4. Syntax and semantics are not closely related and are distinct.

5. It is generally agreed that there are five major stages in language development.

6. Cooing begins at about 10 weeks.

7. By about one month, babies are able to distinguish between phenomes and other sounds.

8. Cooing does not occur when babies are hungry, tired or in pain.

9. Complete mastery of phenomes is achieved around 10 years.

10. Phonetic contraction whereby phenome production is restricted to those used in baby's native language, begins around 10 months.

11. Token test is a test of language.

12. Kendrick battery is a test of language.

13. Marie's Three Paper Test is widely employed for the rapid assessment of serious comprehension defects.

14. Dominant hemisphere is responsible for the insertion and interpretation of the emotional inflexions of speech.

15. In conduction aphasia, comprehension and verbal fluency is not affected.

16. Transcortical aphasia can be both sensory and motor.

17. Anomic aphasia is caused by localized dominant angular gyrus damage.

18. Thalamic aphasia is caused by non-dominant thalamus lesion.

19. Global aphasia occurs because of partial left hemisphere dysfunction.

20. According to Chomsky, aspects of language like grammar are acquired rather than innate.

21. Regarding language, pragmatics means the rules whereby words are ordered to form sentences.

22. Regarding language, semantics is the study of the meaning of words.

23. Regarding language, 'transformational grammar' is a weak syntactic system.

24. According to Chomsky, at a superficial syntactic level all languages have lot of common things.

25. Regarding, language comprehension, 'anaphoric reference' means the decision to attach noun to which pronoun.

26. Regarding language, 'anaphoric reference' deficits are sometimes important in schizophrenia.

27. According to Austin, the literal meaning of what we say conveys the illocutionary force.

28. According to Austin, utterances which convey an intended meaning through the non-literal meaning of the utterance is called illocutionary force.

29. According to Austin, utterances have affect on the listener and that aspect of the utterance is called prelocutionary force of the utterance.

30. Regarding speech production, lexicon is the hypothesised mental construct resembling a dictionary.

31. Modern speech theorists agree with Freud that everyday slips of the tongue occur because of speakers repressed intention.

32. According to speech theorists, word substitution errors arise at one of the four stages.

33. According to speech theorists, the two stages at which word substitution errors arise are dependent on each other.

34. According to Chomsky, language develops independently of other non-linguistic cognitive processes.

35. According to Chomsky, language has its own independent and separate genetic roots in an inborn 'language acquisition device'.

36. According to Vygotsky language and thought have distinct roots.

37. According to Sapir-Whorf hypothesis, language determines thought.

38. The dual-code theory of language states that codes or representations for storing images and words are representationally distinct.

39. Regarding language, the decompositional view states that the meaning of words consists of a number of semantic features.

40. In problem solving, algorithms can be less time consuming when the number of possible solutions is large.

41. According to logicians, the strongest arguments are inductively valid.

42. According to logicians, it is improbable that the conclusion is false, if the argument is inductively strong.

43. Regarding problem solving, functional fixedness is a type of mental set in which we see that an object may have functions or uses other than its normal ones.

44. Heuristics are rules which guarantee a solution to the problems.

45. Regarding problem solving, algorithms guarantee solutions.

46. According to Chomsky, development of language is independent of other non-linguistic cognitive processes.

47. Chomsky stated that transformational grammar is responsible for creating new sentences.

48. Regarding language development, Vygotsky stated that language and thought are dependent on each other.

49. It is rare for right-handed people to be right hemisphere dominant for language.

50. Brocha's aphasia is characterized by impaired verbal fluency, impaired auditory comprehension, and impaired repetition.

●————————————————●

3. LANGUAGE AND THOUGHT
ANSWERS

1. True.
2. True.
3. True.
4. False. Although distinct, they are closely related.
5. False. There are three stages.
6. False. 6 weeks.
7. True.
8. True. It is associated with pleasurable states.
9. False. Around 7 years.
10. True.
11. True.
12. False. It is for object learning and psychomotor speed for use with elderly subjects.
13. False. For mild comprehension defects of speech.
14. False. Non-dominant.
15. True.
16. True.
17. True.
18. False. Dominant.
19. False. Total.
20. False. They are innate.
21. False. How we use language.
22. True.
23. False. It is a very powerful system.
24. False. At deep level.
25. True.

26. False. Often important.

27. False. Locutionary force.

28. True.

29. True.

30. True.

31. False. They view them as transient difficulties in the speech production system.

32. False. One of two stages.

33. False. They are independent.

34. True.

35. True.

36. True.

37. True.

38. True.

39. True.

40. False. Time consuming in these situations.

41. False. Deductively valid.

42. True.

43. False. Functional fixedness is a hindrance in problem solving because we fail to appreciate the possibility of other functions or uses.

44. False. These rules result in reaching solutions quickly.

45. True.

46. True

47. True

48. False. They develop independently.

49. True. It occurs in approximately 1 percent of the cases.

50. False. Auditory comprehension is intact.

●────────────────●

4. ATTENTION AND MEMORY

1.   The two stage theory accounts for the superiority of recall over recognition.

2.   Recognition memory is consistently superior to retrieval of information.

3.   Retrieval of information involves explicit memory.

4.   Ribot's law is a concept of memory.

5.   The primacy affect means that items learnt first in a sequence are recalled better than those at the end.

6.   Recency effect means the words that are learned first are retained longer.

7.   Episodic and semantic memory is types of declarative memory.

8.   Regarding chunking in memory, the number of chunks and their contents is restricted.

9.   Sensory memory lasts for 0.5 minute.

10. Visual sensory memory is called iconic memory.

11. Sensory memory for auditory information is called echoic memory.

12. Regarding memory, items that are intermediate are least likely to be recalled accurately.

13. Regarding memory, retrieval requires effort.

14. Regarding memory, semantic encoding is a more effective way than simply rehearsing information from the short term memory.

15. Theoretically long-term memory has unlimited capacity.

16. Emotional factors can influence retrieval from long-term memory.

17. Regarding memory, retrieval is facilitated by emotionally

charged situations.

18. Regarding memory emotionally charged situations are rehearsed and organized in a better way than non-emotionally charged ones.

19. Regarding memory, repression of emotionally charged material facilitates retrieval.

20. Forgetting is usually due to storage failure rather than retrieval failure.

21. According to interference theory (proactive interference) of forgetting, previous learning is likely to impair subsequent learning.

22. According to retroactive interference theory of forgetting, previous learning is likely to impair new learning.

23. According to decay theory of forgetting, forgetting is dependent on the amount of material accumulated in long-term memory.

24. Regarding divided attention, the performance of two simultaneous tasks is often efficient provided the two tasks are different.

25. The loss of performance in two different tasks is called 'dual task interference'.

26. Regarding attention and memory, all processing is conscious.

27. Sometimes people can be remarkably good at dual-task performance.

28. There is reasonable agreement between researchers that there are two domains of processing sensory data.

29. According to Gestalt psychology, features which are close together tend to be analysed as a part of a single perceptual object.

30. Features which are close together tend to be analysed as part of a single perceptual object. This kind of processing is called 'post-attentive'.

31. Stage models of attention suggest that selectivity can be modelled in terms of a 'bottleneck' in the later stages of processing.

32. Research suggests that there may be dual task interference at both perceptual and response selection stages of processing.

33. Regarding attention simple stage processing assume that processing is data driven.

34. Research has shown that both voluntary and involuntary processes contribute to attention.

35. The major application of capacity theory regarding attention has been to sustained attention.

36. Regarding attention, levels of control models suggests that processing is parallel rather than serial.

37. Regarding attention, levels of control models suggests that there are low and upper level systems.

38. The latest model of memory is the modal memory.

39. The traditional model of memory, the modal model has been discarded as its constructs are no more useful.

40. According to Baddeley, working memory consists of a modality-free central executive controlling an articulatory loop.

41. Declarative knowledge is then ability to perform a skilled task.

42. Declarative knowledge is knowing factual information which can be easily articulated.

43. Anderson made the distinction between episodic memory and semantic memory.

44. Anderson made the distinction procedural and declarative knowledge.

45. Semantic memory refers to stored factual knowledge.

46. Episodic memory is the day to day working memory.

47. Tulving formulated the encoding specificity principle.

48. Tulving's theory of encoding specificity principle explains why cues are helpful when trying to recall something.

49. According to Tulving's encoding specificity principle, the probability of an item's retrieval given a specific cue depends on the retrieval cue being incorporated into the memory during encoding.

50. According to 'generate and recognise' model, memory consists of passive collections of concepts stored away.

51. Regarding memory, organisation, elaboration and integration of material contribute towards good memory.

52. The average short-term memory has a digit span of '7 plus or minus 2'.

53. Regarding memory, retroactive interference is the deleterious effect of new learning upon retrieval of old information.

54. Regarding memory, proactive inhibition is the inhibitory effect of previously learned information upon new learning.

55. Memory is sensitive to the circumstance of learning but not retrieval.

56. Memory is affected by the nature of the material and is poor if it is unpredictable.

57. The capacity of short term memory can be increased if separate pieces of information were combined into a larger piece of information.

58. Interference theory of forgetting suggests that metabolic processes occur over time which degrade the engram resulting in the memory contained within it becoming unavailable.

59. Retroactive inhibition suggests that previous learning impairs subsequent learning.

60. Bilateral damage to the hippocampus produces retrograde amnesia.

61. Endorphins are involved in memory processes.

62. The short-term memory has a capacity of seven chunks.

63. According to research, REM sleep is required for long-term consolidation of memory.

64. Recent research regarding focused attention suggests that alternative information is processed simultaneously.

65. According to Hebb's consolidation theory, there is storage or registration deficit in amnesia.

66. Regarding attention, dual-task interference means that during divided attention there is no loss of performance.

67. Episodic memory is part of long-term memory.

68. Explicit memory requires the cerebellum needs to be intact.

69. Recent research regarding attention, supports Broadbent's idea of filter that selects a limited stimuli.

70. In Broadbent's conceptualization of selective attention, there are three dimensions: filtering, categorizing and pigeonholing.

71. An ability to sustain attention is called vigilance.

72. The ability to hear one's name called out by a nonattended voice in a crowded and noisy room is an example of focal attention.

73. Regarding attention capacity, focal attention requires cognitive effort and have high processing demand.

74. Long-term memory is thought to have an associative or schematic organization that influences the processes of encoding and retrieval.

75. Regarding attention capacity, parallel processes have low or no processing capacity demands.

●————————————●

4. ATTENTION AND MEMORY
ANSWERS

1. False.
2. False.
3. True.
4. True. Also known as Law of Regression. Remote memories remain intact until later stages of degenerative diseases.
5. False. The other way round.
6. False. Primary effect.
7. True.
8. False. Contents are not restricted.
9. False. 0.5 seconds
10. True.
11. True.
12. True.
13. False.
14. True.
15. True.
16. True.
17. True.
18. True.
19. False. Hinders retrieval.
20. False. Vice versa.
21. True.
22. False. New learning is likely to impair previous learning.
23. False. Forgetting is time dependent.
24. False. Often inefficient.
25. True.

26. False.

27. True.

28. True.

29. True.

30. False. Pre-attentive.

31. True.

32. True.

33. True.

34. True.

35. False. Divided attention.

36. False. Serial.

37. True.

38. False. This is the traditional model.

39. False. Constructs are still useful.

40. True.

41. False. This is procedural knowledge.

42. True.

43. False. It was Tulving.

44. True.

45. True.

46. True.

47. True.

48. True.

49. True.

50. True.

51. True.

52. True.

53. True.

54. True.

55. False. It is sensitive to both

56. True.
57. True
58. False. This is Decay theory.
59. False. Later learning interferes with the recall of earlier learning.
60. True
61. False.
62. True.
63. True.
64. True.
65. True.
66. False. There is loss of performance.
67. True.
68. False. This is required for implicit memory. For explicit memory, medial temporal lobes need to be intact.
69. False. Recent research deemphasizes this idea.
70. True.
71. True.
72. False. This is an example of an ongoing parallel attention processes.
73. True.
74. True
75. True.

5. NEUROPSYCHOLOGY, CONSCIOUSNESS AND UNCONSCIOUSNESS PROCESS

1. Dyslexias are inborn disorders of reading.
2. Lexicon is the mental dictionary where all our knowledge about word meaning and pronunciation is stored.
3. Graphemes are the visual spelling units of a language.
4. Phonemes are the units of sound of a language.
5. Regarding dyslexias, the lexical-route is used for assembling pronunciations out of individual letter-to-sound correspondences.
6. Attentional dyslexia is an example of deep dyslexia.
7. Deep dyslexia is characterised by the presence of semantic reading errors.
8. Semantic reading errors are called 'paralexias'.
9. Visual dyslexia is an example of peripheral dyslexias.
10. The speech in Wernickie's aphasia is slow and hesitant.
11. The speech in Brocha's aphasia is rapid and displays lack of syntactic structure.
12. In Wernickie's aphasia neologisms are frequently found.
13. Terms like anomia, nominal aphasia and word amnesia mean the same thing.
14. In agnosia, there is difficulty in retrieving names.
15. In agnosia, there is defect in object perception and comprehension.
16. In agnosia, the impairment can affect visual, auditory or tactile faculties.
17. In prosopagnosia, the patients may be unable their own faces.
18. Prosopagnosia is the inability to recognise familiar faces.
19. Amnesic patients have intact explicit memory but impaired implicit memory.

20. Biological studies indicate that the negative symptoms of schizophrenia may reflect a generalized form of brain damage.

21. Regarding positive symptoms, evidence suggests global changes in neuronal density.

22. Regarding positive symptoms, evidence suggests that the normal pattern of asymmetry in right and left frontal plane is reversed.

23. The left frontal plane is wider than the right frontal plane in normal brains.

24. Regarding schizophrenia, there is evidence of right temporofrontal disturbance.

25. The integrationist model of schizophrenia suggests that there is primary disturbance of function is the result of damage or impairment to the dominant frontotemporal circuitry.

26. According to integrationist model of schizophrenia, there is a faulty communication between the two cerebral systems.

27. Post traumatic amnesia is an accurate predictor of severity and prognosis.

28. In penetrating injuries, post-traumatic amnesia can give a fairly reasonable idea about the prognosis.

29. Galveston Orientation and Amnesic test is for retrograde amnesia.

30. Galveston Orientation and Amnesic test comprises 100 questions.

31. The Wechsler Memory Scale is used to asses post-traumatic amnesia.

32. Most people with nonfluent aphasia are able to produce sentences containing more than four words.

33. In fluent aphasias, the utterances are free from errors in word choice.

34. In conduction aphasia, verbal repetition is slightly impaired.

35. In conduction aphasia, reading comprehension is consistently impaired.

36. Transcortical motor amnesia is a relatively common aphasia syndrome.

37. Patients with Korsakoff's syndrome have permanent short term memory.

38. Clock's drawing test requires the patient to use executive planning.

39. Regarding language, most left-handers have dominant right cerebral hemisphere.

40. Lesions in the Wernickie's area is associated with loss of the ability to understand the written   word.

41. Neuropsychological screening tests typically provide detailed assessments or diagnosis.

42. The 7-Minute Screen is a highly sensitive tool for making initial diagnosis of Alzheimer's disease.

43. Trail making test is one of the subtest of Halstead-Reitan Neuropsychological Test Battery.

44. The 7-Minute Screen (for initial diagnoses of Alzheimer's disease) consists of seven brief tests.

45. Strength of grip is one of the subtests of Halstead-Reitan Neuropsychological Test Battery.

46. Conscious information processing occurs simultaneously on many parallel tracks.

47. Conscious information processing takes place in sequence (serially).

48. Sexual fantasies indicate sexual problems or dissatisfaction.

49. As compared to subconscious, consciousness is slow and has limited capacity.

50. 20 percent of the population fantasizes so vividly that they are called fantasy-prone personalities.

51. Research has established that older people spend more time day dreaming as compared to young.

52. About 95 percent of both men and women have had sexual fantasies.

53. Daydreaming is abnormal and maladaptive.

54. As compared to non-impulsive type, people who indulge in delinquent and violent behaviour have fewer vivid fantasies.

55. Research has shown that on short, highly motivating tasks, sleep deprivation causes adverse effect.

56. Most dreaming occurs in Non-rem sleep.

57. Stage I sleep last for two hours.

58. In Non-Rem sleep, autonomic activity increases.

59. Rem sleep accounts for about 25 percent of all time asleep.

60. Research has established that many people do not dream at all.

61. Stage 3 is marked by sleep spindles and K complexes.

62. During clouding of consciousness there is disorientation in time, place, person and disturbances of perception and attention.

63. Language functions are particularly centred in the temporal lobe.

64. Left-right disorientation occurs in frontal lobe dysfunction.

65. Global amnesia occurs in unilateral lesion of temporal lobe.

66. Disinhibition, euphoria, apathy and loss of initiative are features of frontal lobe dysfunction.

67. Loss of visual perception, visual object agnosia and alexia without agraphia are features of occipital lobe dysfunction.

68. Executive functions are often described correctly as "frontal lobe functions".

69. Boston Diagnostic Aphasia Examination is a test of memory.

70. The Tower of London test is for executive function.

71. The Grooved Pegboard test is used for motor functioning testing.

72. Disruptions of visual perception are limited to patients with lesions of the nondominant hemisphere or with lesions of the parietal cortex.

73. Executive functions include the ability to monitor one's own behaviour, formulate and carry out plans, and process information in sequence.

74. Stupor is characterized the absence or reduction of action and speech.

75. The brainstem reticular formation and the diffuse thalamic projection system activate the cortex to enable the person to relate to his environment (including his inner self).

76. About 80% of right-handed people and most left-handed people have relative language dominance in the left hemisphere.

77. The Serial Sevens Subtraction test assesses a person short term memory and the ability to sustain the task in mind.

78. One short coming of mini-mental state examination is its lack of sensitivity.

79. Prosopagnosia is the inability to recognize familiar and common objects.

80. A neuropsychological consultation is not useful in patients with moderate or severe disability.

81. The assessment of a person's premorbid functioning is essential so that his or her performance other cognitive tests can be interpreted.

82. Assessment of executive functions is technically and theoretically a simple aspect of neuropsychological assessment.

83. Regarding neuropsychological assessment, concentration, comprehension and motivation are important prerequisites for administration of standardized tests.

84. The performance of patients may vary from one testing session to another for a variety of reasons and therefore the neuropsychological assessment may be unreliable.

85. According to Oswald's restoration theory, both REM and NREM sleep help replenish bodily and brain processes.

86. Crick and Mitchison believed that dreams are a way of 'cleaning up' the cortex's neural networks and preparing them for a new input.

•────────────•

5. NEUROPSYCHOLOGY, CONSCIOUSNESS AND UNCONSCIOUSNESS PROCESS
ANSWERS

1. False. Acquired.
2. True.
3. True.
4. True.
5. False. Non-lexical route.
6. False. It is a type of peripheral dyslexia.
7. True.
8. True.
9. True.
10. False. It is rapid and fluent.
11. False. Although it lacks syntactic, it is slow.
12. False. Found sometimes.
13. True.
14. False. This is called anomia.
15. True.
16. True.
17. True.
18. True.
19. False. The other way round.
20. True.
21. False. Does not suggest.
22. True
23. False. Other way round.
24. False. Left temporofrontal disturbance.
25. False. This is called unilaterist model.
26. True.

27. True.

28. False. In closed or blunt injuries it can give a good idea.

29. False.

30. False.

31. True.

32. False. Rare.

33. False. Marred by word error.

34. False. Markedly impaired.

35. False. Nearly normal.

36. False. Uncommon.

37. True

38. False. Although simple to administer, it requires integration of many different cognitive mechanism.

39. False. About 60% of left-handers have dominant left hemisphere.

40. True.

41. False. They provide useful first step in determining what sorts of assessments are needed or justified.

42. True.

43. True. Other major subtests include Category test, Tactual performance, Speech sounds test, Rhythm test, Finger Oscillation test, Reitan-Indiana Aphasia Screening test, Reitan-Klove Lateral Domnance test and Strength of grip test.

44. False. There are four brief tests that focus on orientation, memory, visuospatial skills and expressive language.

45. True.

46. False. Unconscious processing.

47. True.

48. False.

49. True.

50. False. Four percent.

51. False. Young people daydream more.

52. True.

53. False. It can be adaptive and creative.

54. True

55. False.

56. False. REM sleep.

57. False. Few minutes.

58. False. REM sleep.

59. True.

60. False. Everyone dreams but many people do not remember their dreams.

61. False. Stage 2.

62. True

63. True.

64. False. Parietal lobe dysfunction.

65. False. Bilateral lesions.

66. True.

67. True.

68. False. Many patients with non-frontal lobe disorders show executive deficits E.g Parkinson's disease and Huntington's disease.

69. False. It is used to assess language abilities.

70. True.

71. True.

72. False. Occur in many other disorders as well, e.g., lesions of either the dominant or nondominant posterior cortex (parietal, temporal, or occipital).

73. True.

74. True.

75. True.

76. False. About 99% of right handed people and most left-handed people.

77. False. Not a test for memory.

78. True. There is high rate of false-negatives results associated with its use.

79. False. Inability to recognize familiar faces.

80. True.

81. True. Inferences about possible decline in function can also be made.

82. False. It is a complex task.

83. True. The patient must be able to concentrate for at least the time needed to administer the test and must also be able to comprehend the task instructions for any test given. Similarly, the patient may experience an inability to initiate action unless prompted at every stage.

84. True.

85. True.

86. True. They stated this in their reverse learning theory.

6. PERCEPTION

1. Perceptual constancy has been demonstrated for height as well as depth.

2. Absolute threshold can be measured by the method of descending limits.

3. Perception at the absolute threshold is the highest intensity of a stimulus that can be tolerated.

4. Dichotic listening can investigate selective attention.

5. Absolute threshold is the maximum energy required to activate the sensory organ. True

6. Fetcher's Law states that sensory perception is a logarithmic function of stimulus intensity.

7. Signal detection theory holds that perception depends solely on stimulus intensity.

8. Regarding depth perception, a three dimensional visual perception is formed from two-dimensional retinal images.

9. Perceptual set is a motivational state of mind in which certain aspects of stimuli are perceived according to expectation.

10. According to Gestalt psychology, law of continuity states that like items are grouped together.

11. Regarding development of visual perception, size and shape constancy, depth perception and shape discrimination are believed to be innate.

12. Regarding attention, stroop effect means that the automatic process is so ingrained that it interferes with controlled processing.

13. Regarding attention, performance deteriorates during in sustained attention.

14. Regarding information processing, conceptually driven processing applies when data input is incomplete.

15. In divided attention, loss of performance is called dual-task interference.

16. Weber's law does not hold when stimuli are very intense or very weak.

17. Regarding depth perception, monocular cues can only be used with one eye.

18. Motion parallax is a binocular cue.

19. Accommodation, convergence and stereopsis are cues which can be used only by those looking at the world with both eyes together.

20. According to Marr's theory of visual perception, visual perception involves producing three detailed description of the visual environment.

21. Marr's theory of visual perception has been very influential.

22. According to Biederman's theory of object recognition, there are 86 basic shapes or components.

23. Regarding colour perception, yellow tennis balls are difficult to see than white ones.

24. Regarding perception, Bottom-up processing means that perception is influenced by expectations, stored knowledge and context etc.

25. In perception, Bottom-up processing implies that perception depends directly on external stimuli.

26. According to Marr's theory of visual perception, there are four stages.

27. Depth perception involves object interposition.

28. Regarding attention, dual-task interference means that during divided attention there is no loss of performance.

29. Sensation is the secondary encoding of simple sensory data from peripheral sensory organs to sensory memory.

30. Retinal disparity refers to the slightly different view of the world registered by each eye.

31. Perception takes into account experiences stored in our memory, the context in which the sensation occurs and our emotions and motivations.

32. The data collected about the world through our senses is in three dimensions.

33. Where an object is superimposed upon another, the superimposed object will appear to be nearer.

34. The Prototype models theory of pattern recognition hypothesizes that templates are stored in memory against which images are matched.

35. According to feature-analysing theory of pattern recognition, features of objects Stored in memory are scanned for recognition.

36. Gregory's theory of perception states that the process of perception is an active one.

37. The Prototype model theory of pattern recognition states that objects in the world around are in a sense reflections of idealized prototypes and it id these prototypes which are stored in memory.

38. Law of Pragnanz is a Gestalt principle of perceptual organization.

39. Gibson's theory of direct perception could be described as combination of top-down and bottom-up processing theory.

40. Analysis by synthesis is a perceptual model where information is extracted from he environment through the senses to correct and update impressions of what the environment might be like.

41. Perceptual defence is a general term for a whole range of emotional, motivational, social and cultural factors which can influence cognition.

42. Witkin identified three different cognitive styles which relate to different ways of perceiving.

43. Habituation technique is used to assess perception of adults based upon the length of time they fixate on an object before becoming bored with it and look away.

44. Visual cliff is an apparatus to test the extent to which babies and small animals are able to perceive depth.

45. According to Helmholtz's theory of perception, perception consists of two stages, the first is analytic stage and the second is synthetic stage.

46. The Gestalt approach to perception opposes the role of innate processes in perception.

47. Regarding attentional processes, Broadbent's theory states that the mind has an unlimited capacity to carry out complete processing.

48. Regarding motion perception, induced motion is a type of illusion.

49. Orientation constancy is the ability to recognize the true orientation of the figure in the real world, even though its orientation in the retinal image is changed.

50. Briderman has proposed that all objects can be assembled from a set of geometrical ions or gems.

•——————————————•

6. PERCEPTION
ANSWERS

1. True.
2. False. Ascending limits.
3. False. Lowest intensity.
4. True.
5. True.
6. True.
7. False. Other factors such as motivation.
8. True.
9. True.
10. False. Law of Similarity.
11. False. Have to be learnt.
12. True.
13. True.
14. True.
15. True.
16. True.
17. False. Can be used with both eyes.
18. False. Monocular cue.
19. True.
20. True. Primal sketch, two and half D Sketch, and 3-D model representation.
21. True.
22. False. He claimed there were approximately 36 basic shapes which he called 'geons'. For example, spheres, cylinders, and blocks.
23. False. Yellow balls are easy to see.
24. False. This is top-down processing.

25. True.
26. True. There are four successive stages that which represent individual visual modules of progressive complexity.
27. True.
28. False. Performance is deteriorated
29. False. It is the initial encoding.
30. True.
31. True.
32. False. It is n two dimensions but the interpretation of this data within the brain results in three dimensions.
33. True.
34. False. This is Template matching theory.
35. True.
36. True.
37. True.
38. True. It states that psychological organization will always be as good as the prevailing principles allow.
39. False. This is Neisser's cyclical theory of perception. Gibson's theory states that there need not be processing stages interposed between the light falling on the retina and responses made by the organism as a result.
40. True.
41. False. This is called Set. Perceptual defence is a predisposition not to perceive something because of unpleasant emotional overtones.
42. False. Two styles, field-dependence and field-independence which relate to different ways of perceiving and are linked to personality characteristics.
43. False. Used in infants.
44. True.
45. True.
46. False. It supports this idea.

47. False. The mind has only limited capacity.
48. True.
49. True.
50. True.

7. MOTIVATION & EMOTION

1. According to intrinsic motivation theories, needs arise to maintain biological homeostasis.

2. According to extrinsic motivation theories secondary drives are acquired by learning.

3. Hull's drive-reduction theory is on of the extrinsic theories of motivation.

4. Mowrer's theory of motivation describes primary drives.

5. Woodworth defined drive in biological terms as energy released from an organism's store.

6. Regarding motivation, Mowrer proposed the notion of secondary drives which result from generalization and conditioning.

7. Regarding motivation, Hull developed a theory in which primary biological drives are activated by needs which arise from homeostatic imbalance.

8. Extrinsic theories of motivation propose that the activity engaged in has its own reward.

9. According to optimal arousal theory of motivation, a high level of arousal leads to optimal performance.

10. Maslow's theory of motivation includes both extrinsic and intrinsic theories.

11. Festinger's cognitive dissonance is a form of intrinsic motivation theory.

12. According to theories of motivation, anxiety is a secondary drive.

13. Drive reduction relates to extrinsic motivation.

14. Cognitive processes in emotion are postulated in the James-Lange Theory of Emotion.

15. Love, disgust and anger are primary emotions.

16. According to James-Lange theory of emotion, perception of an emotion-arousing stimulus causes physiological changes.

17. According to Cannon-Bard theory of emotion, perception of emotion-arousing stimulus leads to the concurrent experience of emotion and physiological responses.

18. Schacter's cognitive labelling theory is regarding emotion.

19. According to Cannon-Bard theory, the experience of emotion is secondary to the somatic responses to the perception of given emotionally significant events.

20. According to James-Lange theory of emotion, the perception of an emotionally important event both the somatic responses and the experience of emotion occur together.

21. The influence of cognitive factors on the conscious experience of emotion was demonstrated in an experiment by Cannon and Bard.

22. According to Vaughan and Leff, high expressed emotions (when patient is in contact with relatives for more than 35 hours per week) are a better predictor of relapse than non-compliance with medication.

23. The amygdala and hypothalamus are involved in aggression.

24. Aggression is more likely to occur following an expected failure than an unexpected one.

25. Regarding emotion, the James-Lange theory emphasized the importance of physiological responses.

26. According to Plutchick, love is a secondary emotion.

27. According to Cannon-Bard theory, events are first processed at various centres in the brain, which then direct the simultaneous reactions of arousal, behavioural action, and emotional experience.

28. Research has shown that different emotions show different patterns of autonomic responses.

29. Emotions show different patterns of similar autonomic activity across different cultures.

30. Amygdala plays an especially important in attaching meaning to positive emotions and experiences.

31. PET studies have shown that happiness and sadness are opposite responses in the same portions of the cortex.

32. The frequent and uncontrollable emotional outbursts of infants arise because of the parts of the parts of cortex that control emotional responding are not fully developed until sometimes between 36 and 48 months.

33. Cannon and colleagues have emphasized that visceral activity is irrelevant for emotional experience.

34. According to Cognitive Appraisal Theory of emotions, stimulus events and physiological arousal are cognitively appraised simultaneously.

35. The Cannon-Bard theory of emotions predicts independence between bodily and psychological responses.

36. Lazarus has stated that cognitive appraisal of emotions often involve conscious thought.

37. According to Schacter, the experience of emotion is the combined effect of physiological arousal and cognitive appraisal.

38. Research suggests that the relationship between arousal and performance follows an inverted U-shaped function.

39. Bower has proposed that when a person experiences a given emotion in a particular situation, that emotion is stored in memory along with the ongoing events, as part of the same context.

40. Yerkes-Dodson Law states that performance of difficult tasks decreases as arousal increases, whereas performance of easy tasks increases as arousal increases.

41. Material that is congruent with one's prevailing mood is more likely to be noticed, attended to, and processed more deeply.

42. Mood-dependent memory refers to situations in which people find it difficult to recall information when their mood at retrieval matches their mood when they first

committed the information to memory.

43. According to Reversal theory of emotion, the contrasting state of Conformist is Non-conformist.

44. Hull emphasized the role of tension in motivation.

45. Reversal theory of motivation suggests four pairs of metamotivational states. of the opposing states.

46. Michael Apter's theory of motivation supports the idea of motivation as tension reduction.

47. According to Reversal theory of motivation, the states of Autic and Alloic are contrasted.

48. Rotter postulated that the outcome of behaviour can be attributed to dispositional factors or to situational f actors.

49. Maslow believed that there are two kinds of motivation, deficiency motivation and growth motivation.

50. According to Maslow's hierarchy of needs, love and belonging needs are above the esteem needs.

●————————————————●

7. MOTIVATION & EMOTION
ANSWERS

1.   False. Extrinsic theories.
2.   True.
3.   True.
4.   False. Secondary drives
5.   True.
6.   True.
7.   True.
8.   False. Intrinsic theories propose this.
9.   False.   High and low levels of arousal lead to reduce performance.
10. True.
11. True.
12. True.
13. False. emotion and somatic response occur simultaneously.
14. True.
15. False. Not love.
16. True.
17. True.
18. True.
19. False. James-Lange Theory.
20. False. Cannon-Bard Theory.
21. False. By Schachter and Singer.
22. True.
23. True.
24. False.
25. True.

26. True.

27. True.

28. True.

29. True. Research performed by Paul Ekman and colleagues show this.

30. False. Negative experiences.

31. False. The opposite emotions have activities in the different parts of the brain.

32. False. The relevant parts develop between 18 and 36 months.

33. True.

34. True. This is according to the situational cues and context factors, with the emotional experience resulting from the interaction of the level of arousal and the nature of appraisal.

35. True

36. False. Often occurs without conscious thought.

37. True.

38. True. Too little or too much arousal may impair performance.

39. True.

40. True.

41. True

42. False. They find it easier.

43. False. It is negativistic.

44. True

45. True. This theory attempts to explain human motivation in terms of reversals from one to the other of the opposing states.

46. False. It rejects this idea.

47. True. In Autic the primary concern is with oneself whereas in Alloic it is with others.

48. False. Heider stated this. Rotter emphasized the importance of expectations in motivating behaviour.

49.   True.

50.   False. Esteem needs are higher than the love and belonging needs.

———————————

8. INTELLIGENCE

1. The Wechsler and the Stanford-Binet tests correlate well.

2. The Raven's matrices test correlates highly with IQ scores.

3. The Raven's matrices test is scored as a percentile.

4. An association between birth order and intelligence has been convincingly demonstrated.

5. In depression, performance tests are more impaired than verbal tests.

6. Intelligent tests can accurately diagnose specific brain damage.

7. The Kendrick battery test is useful for young people.

8. Childhood IQ predicts adult intellectual behaviour in precise way.

9. In girls there is greater variance of intelligence than boys.

10. Boys do relatively better than girls on the verbal abilities sub scale of Wechsler intelligence scale for children.

11. There is an inverse correlation between intelligence and age.

12. Sampling procedures for standardization of IQ include socioeconomic status.

13. Crystallized intelligence decreases with age.

14. Fluid intelligence results from accumulated knowledge and result of education, experience and cultural background.

15. Fluid intelligence is used in novel situations or problems.

16. Spearman proposed a general factor of intelligence.

17. Thurstone identified five primary mental abilities.

18. According to Guildford, there are 100 factors of intelligence

19. The seven primary mental abilities identified by Thurston correlate with each other.

20. Cattell proposed theory of crystallized and fluid intelligence

21. According to Carroll's hierarchical model of intelligence, there are seven factors at the intermediate level of the hierarchy.

22. Gardner proposed five different intelligencies.

23. The Componential sub theory, proposed by Sternberg, deals with the individual's external world.

24. According to Sternberg's Triarchic theory, different forms of intelligence are relatively independent of each other.

25. The Wechsler Adult Intelligent Scale-Revised (WAIS-R) generates five scaled score.

26. There is high correlation between any two items of Wechsler Adult Intelligence Scale.

27. Spearman's theory of intelligence implies that a good intelligence test will be highly g (general intelligence) loaded.

28. According to Spearman's theory of intelligence, important or meaningful individual differences in test performance are due to solely to individual differences in general intelligence factor, g.

29. Crystallized intelligence refers to the size of one's store of factual knowledge.

30. Spearman's theory of intelligence suggests that a good measure of g (general intelligence) will successfully predict performance of all cognitively demanding tasks.

31. Minnesota Multiphasic Personality Inventory contains items dealing with sex, religion, bladder control and family relations.

32. The Kaufman Assessment Battery for Children attempts to separate fluid and crystallized intelligence.

33. Sternberg's contextual theory of intelligence deals with the basic cognitive processes involved in knowledge acquisition and performance.

34. A test with low g (general intelligence) loading should predict an extremely wide range of "intelligent "behaviours.

35. Fluid intelligence refers to an individual's acquired knowledge and skills.

36. Fluid and crystallized intelligence measures are poorly correlated.

37. In his structure of intellect model, Guilford stated that there are six types of operations, five types of content and six types of products.

38. Test-retest reliability is established by administering the measure to a group of subjects on two occasions separated by a designated period of time.

39. There is evidence that fluid and crystallized intelligence show same developmental trends.

40. Guilford proposes that intelligence is organized according to five dimensions.

41. The importance of g factor (general intelligence) is central to the theories of Spearman, Vernon, and Carroll.

42. Sternberg's triarchic theory of intelligence features four sub theories.

43. Someone's standing on g factor (general intelligence) is the best single predictor of his or her performance at school, job etc.

44. According to Sternberg, componential theory is concerned with how intelligent behaviour is generated.

45. The Raven's Advanced Progressive Matrices is appropriate for intellectually advanced subjects.

46. The WISC-III consists of 8 verbal scales and 4 performance scales.

47. Sternberg's experiential theory deals with what behaviours are intelligent in what context.

48. The WAIS-III includes 20 separate subtests.

49. The Multidimensional Aptitude Battery is comparable to the WAIS-R in all major aspects.

50. The Raven's Coloured Progressive Matrices is more

appropriate for adults who show signs of retardation.

51. In WAIS-III. there are 10 verbal subtests and 7 performance subtests.

52. Unlike the Stranford-Binet Test t, the WAIS-III can be administered by any psychologist.

53. The WAIC-III (Wechsler Intelligence Scale for Children) consists of 14 subtests.

54. Most IQ tests given today are not individual tests; they are group tests.

55. Some psychologists believe that the IQ differences among children of different ethnic origins have to do more with the socioeconomic differences than ethnicity.

56. Intellectual performance remains the same across all ages when a person has an unlimited time to complete a task.

57. IQ scores from 35-49 suggest severe learning disability.

58. The concept of neural pruning (the decrease in the number of synapses in the brain) is supported by PET scans.

59. Neural pruning appears to be necessary for intellectual development.

60. Algorithms and heuristics guarantee solution to problems.

●————————————●

8. INTELLIGENCE
ANSWER

1. True.

2. True.

3. True.

4. False. Not convincingly.

5. True.

6. False.

7. False. For old people.

8. False.

9. False.

10. False.

11. False. Intelligence increases with age unto certain age.

12. True

13. False. Increases throughout life

14. False. This is crystallized intelligence. Fluid intelligence refers to the ability to solve novel or unusual situations.

15. True.

16. True.

17. False.

18. False. He claimed there are 150 factors of intelligence but had evidence of 100 factors only.

19. True.

20. True.

21. True. Fluid ability, general fluency, general visual perception, general speed, general auditory perception, general memory capacity, and crystallized intelligence.

22. Eight. Seven. Spatial, musical, linguistic, logical-mathematical, interpersonal, intrapersonal, bodily-kinaesthetic intelligence and naturalistic.

23.	False. Deals with the individual's internal world. Contextual sub theory deals with external world.
24.	False. Gardner proposed this. Sternberg emphasized on the ways in which the different components of intelligence complement and work together.
25.	False. Three.
26.	False.
27.	True. This means that the influence of a specific factor or of a measurement error will be minimized.
28.	True.
29.	True.
30.	True.
31.	True. It also contains other potentially sensitive topics.
32.	True.
33.	False. This is componential theory.
34.	False. High g loading.
35.	False. Crystallized intelligence.
36.	False. They are highly correlated.
37.	True.
38.	True.
39.	False. Different developmental trends.
40.	False. Three dimensions: Operations, Contents and Products.
41.	True.
42.	False. Three: Componential theory, contextual theory and experiential theory.
43.	True
44.	True.
45.	True.
46.	False. 6 verbal and 6 performances.
47.	False. This is contextual theory.

48. False. 14 subtests. 11 are used in computing a full scale IQ score, a Verbal IQ score, and a performance IQ score.

49. True.

50. True. Also for children from 4-10 years.

51. False. 7 verbal and 7 performance subtests.

52. False. Both are administered by specially trained psychologists.

53. False. 12 subtests. The adult version contains 14 subtests.

54. True. Although individual IQ tests are useful in making diagnostic decisions, they are time consuming and expensive.

55. False. Most psychologists believe this.

56. True

57. False. Moderate learning disability.

58. True.

59. True. Mechanism of neural pruning is, however, unclear.

60. False. Algorithms guarantee a solution but are time consuming. Heuristics don't guarantee a solution but can help produce solutions more quickly.

9. PERSONALITY

1. Coping in severely stressful situations is influenced more by immediate situational factors than by general coping styles.
2. Longitudinal studies have demonstrated a consistency in personality traits.
3. Specific behaviours may be confidently predicted from formally assessed personality measures.
4. Fairly consistent associations are evident between specific personality measures and certain psychiatric disorders.
5. Eysenck's theory of personality is a nomothetic type theory.
6. Kelly proposed an idiographic theory of personality.
7. Cattell proposed an idiographic theory of personality.
8. Personal construct theory suggests that personality is the sum of a cluster of neurotic complexes.
9. Personal construct theory suggests that people may sacrifice themselves to preserve core constructs.
10. The Minnesota multiphase personality has a schizophrenia scale.
11. The California personality inventory was developed for a psychiatric population
12. Traits show little consistency over time.
13. Personal construct theory proposes personality in terms of defences.
14. Personal construct theory includes social and moral constructs as determining influences of personality.
15. Implicit personality theory describes how our core personality traits develop.
16. According to Kelly's personal construct theory, an individual has core constructs, both conscious and unconscious.

17. According to Erikson's theory of psychosexual development, initiative/guilt occurs at 6-12 years.

18. Eysenck's personality theory derived 16 personality factors.

19. Minnesota multiphase personality inventory is interviewer rated inventory.

20. Maudsley Personality inventory is a projective test.

21. According to Jungian personality theory, the inward flow of libido towards the depth of the psyche is known as introversion.

22. Extroverts are characterized by habitual outgoingness and venturing with careless confidence into the unknown.

23. According to the psychoanalytic theory of development of personality, the development of personality is complete within the first 7 years of life.

24. The California psychological inventory is a test of personality.

25. The Rorschach inkblot test is a test of personality.

26. In his theory of personality, Jung described "introversion" and "extraversion".

27. Regarding personality, trait theories employ a normothetic approach.

28. In his theory of personality, Eysenck used a 'dimensional' approach.

29. The construct repertory grid can be used to explore both conscious and unconscious traits.

30. Costa and McCrea described three universal factors.

31. The Minnesota Multiphasic Personality Inventory has five clinical scales and three validity scales.

32. Adler postulated the principle of dynamism , which in every individual is future directed and moves towards a goal.

33. Self-psychology is a separate movement within psychoanalysis.

34. Kohut argued that narcissism went through the same line of development as object libido and object relations.

35. Kohut bases his self-psychology on the need, only during the course of development.

36. Adolf Mayer opposed the Krapelinian view of mental illness as a having a predetermined identified syndromes.

37. According to Adler, moving from a sense of inferiority to a sense of adequacy is the important motivational motif in life.

38. Adolf Meyer believed that individual's habitual reactions patterns made them more susceptible to specific types of mental illnesses.

39. Karen Horney believed that personality development results from the interaction of biological and psychosocial forces that are unique for each individual.

40. Gordon Allport interpreted personality in motivational terms.

41. George Kelly argued that human beings should be seen as scientists trying to make sense of their world.

42. Berne divided the human psyche into three primary parts: child, parent and adult.

43. Erich Fromm defined personality as the "relatively enduring pattern of interpersonal relations which characterize a human life".

44. In his theory of personality, Reich argued that character armor is comprised of involuntary, repetitive, ego-syntonic behaviours that prevent the emergence of repressed impulses.

45. In his theory of personality, Franz Alexander psychoanalytic thought to patho-physiological Processes.

46. Five-Factor Model of personality was proposed by Tupes and Christal.

47. Allport believed that traits were changeable features of individuals and could not be relied upon to describe individuals.

48. The five-factor model of personality theory includes neuroticism, extroversion, openness, agreeableness and conscientiousness.

49. Cloninger's Temprament and Character Inventory (TCI) consists of ten factors that are intended to assess temperament and five that assess character.

50. Most people can be classified into introverts or extroverts.

●━━━━━━━━━●

9. PERSONALITY
ANSWER

1. True.
2. True.
3. False.
4. False.
5. True.
6. True.
7. True.
8. False.
9. False.
10. True.
11. True.
12. False.
13. False.
14. False.
15. False. This theory explains the unconscious processes that enable us to form impressions of others based on very little evidence.
16. True.
17. True.
18. False. Cattel's Trait Theory.
19. False. Self-reported inventory.
20. False.
21. True.
22. True.
23. False.
24. True.
25. True.

26. True.

27. True.

28. True.

29. False. (Only conscious traits) Is used to interpret or construe one's world.

30. False. Five factors: neuroticism, extroversion, openness, agreeableness, and consciousness

31. False. It has 10 clinical scales and 3 validity scales.

32. True.

33. True. It was originated by Kohut.

34. False. It develops separately and is independent from object libido and object relations.

35. False. During the course of life as well.

36. True

37. True

38. True

39. True

40. False. Abraham Maslow did this.

41. True

42. True

43. False. It was Harry Stack Sullivan. Fromm argued that each person struggles to recapture the state of blissful union that existed parentally.

44. True

45. True. He laid the groundwork for psychosomatic medicine, behavioural medicine, and psychophysiology.

46. True

47. False. Allport asserted that traits were concrete features of individuals that uniquely described them.

48. True. The contemporary five factor theorists, however, differ some what on their conceptualizations of the factors and consequently give them some what different labels.

49.   False.   Four factors assess temperament and three assess character.

50.   False. Most people are ambiverts, and show some of the characteristics of both categories.

10. PSYCHOLOGICAL ASSESSMENT AND PSYCHOMETRY

1. Girls have higher IQ scores in childhood.
2. Boys have a greater range of IQ than girls.
3. Girls have better vocabulary than boys.
4. Personality can be measured by the Repertory Grid Test.
5. The Sentence Completion Test is a personality test.
6. The Likert Scale is more sensitive than the Thurstone scale.
7. The Thurstone Scale is a 5-point scale where the subject is presented with a number of statements.
8. Gollin's figures primarily tests language.
9. Rey- Osterrieth test is a test of personality.
10. The Hidden Figures test is a test of field dependency.
11. The Parental Bonding Instrument measures bonding from the patient's point of view.
12. The Parental Bonding Instrument is based on 35 questions.
13. Thurstone developed the concept of general intelligence factor (g).
14. Spearman proposed primary mental abilities.
15. Crystallized intelligence is used novel situations or problems.
16. Concept of mental age (measure of intellectual ability) was proposed by Binet.
17. Measured intelligence increases upto 20 years of age.
18. Measured intelligence plateaus from 16 years to 30 years.
19. WAIS consists of 5 verbal and 6 performance subtests.
20. National Adult Reading test represents pre-morbid IQ.
21. Mill Hill Vocabulary test is based on recognition and recall.
22. Raven's progressive matrices test involves diagram completion.
23. Wechsler Intelligence Scale for children is from 5 to 15 years.

24. The Wechsler Intelligence Scale consists of 11 sub tests.

25. In Wechsler Intelligence Scale, digit symbol is a verbal type of sub test.

26. The Wechsler Intelligence Scale has a relatively low reliability and validity.

27. The Minnesota Multiphase personality inventory consists of 100 statements concerning attitudes, emotional reactions, physical symptoms and psychological symptoms.

28. California psychological inventory measures 28 traits that are part of normal personality.

29. Eysenck personal questionnaire contains 90 items in true/false format.

30. Projective tests resemble Freud's technique of free association.

31. The Halstead-Reitan Battery can take up to eight hours to administer.

32. The WAIS-R can be viewed as a broad spectrum assessment of cognitive function.

33. In WAIS-R, four of the five performance subscales require a motor input.

34. The WAIS-R subtests are administered in a definable order.

35. The Halstead-Retina Battery comprises 10 components.

36. WAIS is a part of Halstead- Reitan Battery.

37. Minnesota Multiphase Personality Inventory is part of Halstead-Reitan Battery.

38. Finger Oscillation Test is a part of Halstead-Reitan Battery.

39. Tactual Performance Test is part of Halstead-Reitan Battery.

40. The Trail making Test is part of Halstead-Reitan Battery.

41. The Colour Naming Test is part of Halstead-Reitan Battery.

42. The Digit vigilance task is part of Halstead-Reitan Battery.

43. The Rennick Repeatable Battery comprises of 10 sub parts.

44. The Stroop Colour-Word Interference Test comprises five sub parts.

45. The Stroop Colour-Word Interference Test is applicable from 5 to 75 years of age.

46. In the Stroop Colour-Word Interference Test, the subjects reads out from a series of 50 colour-words.

47. The Luria-Nebraska Neuropsychological Battery comprises of 79 items.

48. The Luria-Nebraska Neuropsychological Battery is able to discriminate between organic and non-organic disturbance in more than 80% of cases.

49. In Thematic Apperception Test subjects are asked to write stories on themes suggested by a standard series of drawings.

50. Rorschach inkblot test is an example of projective test.

51. Rorschach inkblot test and Thematic apperception tests have good validity.

52. Analysis of handwriting (graphology) has good validity.

53. In Rorschach inkblot test, the respondent examines ten asymmetrical inkblots and interprets the them.

54. Stroop category test is very sensitive to the presence of brain damage.

55. Stroop category test is very helpful in localizing brain damage.

56. Benton Verbal fluency test is a test of Frontal Lobe Function.

57. Trail making test has low sensitivity for detection of brain damage.

58. The Raven's Progressive Matrices' test is in four versions.

59. In psychological assessment, defensiveness can distort the real information.

60. The California Psychological Inventory is a projective test of personality.

61. Sentence completion test is a projective test of personality.

62. The General Aptitude Test Battery measures two general factors.

63. The Kaufman Assessment Battery for Children is based on research in neurosychology and cognitive psychology.

64. The General Aptitude Test Battery includes only verbal tests.

65. Multidimensional Aptitude Battery consists of verbal and performance batteries.

66. The General Aptitude Test Battery has good reliability and validity.

67. The Black Intelligence Test of Cultural Homogeneity (BITCH) consists of verbal and performance subtests.

68. The Stanford - Binet test includes nonverbal and performance subtests.

69. There are two forms of Raven's Progressive Matrices.

70. The items on California Psychological Inventory are grouped into 20 scales to measure attributes of personality.

71. Scoring the Rorschach Inkblot Test is a simple and quick process.

72. Administration of California Psychological Inventory is laborious and lengthy.

73. California Psychological Inventory is extremely useful in predicting underachievement in academic settings and potential delinquency.

74. The reliability and validity of Rorschach Inkblot test is high.

75. The California Psychological Inventory is a frequently used measure of abnormal personality.

76. The Edwards Personal Preference Schedule attempts to reduce the effects of social desirability in personal assessment.

77. The Sixteen Personality Factor Questionnaire (Fifth Edition) has items grouped into 20 primary factor scales.

78. In Thematic Apperception Test five cards from the total 31 cards are blank to provide maximally ambiguous stimuli.

79. The Rotter Incomplete Sentences Blank Test requires no special training to administer.

80. Administering and scoring of Sixteen Personality Factor Questionnaire requires specially trained psychologist.

81 The Draw a Test requires to draw one human figure.

82. It is possible to achieve the same degree of standardization with all psychological tests.

83. All projective tests share in common the utilization of specific stimuli or tasks.

84. The Rorschach Inkblot test is one of the most widely used structured test for personality assessment.

85. The Rotter Incomplete Sentences Blank test consists of 40 items.

86. Draw -a Person Test is used to assess personality and diagnose psychopathology.

87. The Rorschach Inkblot test consists of a series of 20 bilaterally symmetrical inkblots placed on individual cards.

88. The Thematic Apperception Test consists of 31 cards that contain words concerning relationships or social situations.

89. The Rotter Incomplete Sentences Blank Test is a structured projective test.

90. The Bender Visual Motor Gestalt Test is used in the diagnoses of various types of psychopathology.

91. The Bender Visual-Motor Gestalt Test is useful in the differential diagnosis of perceptual disorders and organic brain disorders.

92. The Bender Visual Motor Gestalt test is a based on the principles of Gestalt psychology.

93. The Bender Visual-Motor Gestalt test is type of projective test.

94. The Paced Auditory Serial Addition Task (PASAT) is a test for divided attention.

95. Test of Everyday Attention (TEA) is a tests attention on the strategic level.

96. In the Six Elements Test (for attention on the strategic level),

subjects are given 10 minutes to perform six tasks.

97. A test's sensitivity or specificity for particular conditions makes it more or less useful, depending on the purpose of the examination.

98. The Spatial Orientation Memory Test is predominantly a measure of visual discrimination and spatial orientation.

99. The Boston Diagnostic Aphasia Examination provides a systematic assessment of communication and communication-related functions in 12 areas defined by factor analysis.

100. The Katz Adjustment Scale: Relatives's Form is appropriate for neuropsychologically impaired patients.

————————•

10. PSYCHOLOGICAL ASSESSMENT AND PSYCHOMETRY
ANSWERS

1.   True.
2.   True.
3.   False.
4.   True.
5.   True.
6.   True.
7.   False.
8.   False. Parietal lobe test.
9.   False. Visual memory test.
10. True.
11. True.
12. False. 25 questions.
13. False. Spearman.
14. False. Thurstone.
15. False. Fluid intelligence.
16. True.
17. False. 16 years.
18. False. Till 25 years.
19. False. Vice versa.
20. True.
21. True.
22. True.
23. True.
24. True.
25. False. Performance Test.
26. False. High reliability and validity.
27. False. 550 statements.

28. False. 18 traits.
29. True.
30. True.
31. True.
32. True.
33. True.
34. True.
35. False. Eleven.
36. True.
37. True.
38. True.
39. True
40. False. This is a part of Rennnick Repeatable Battery.
41. False. This is part of Rennick Repeatable Battery.
42. False. This is part of Rennick Repeatable Battery.
43. False. Seven.
44. False. Three.
45. True.
46. False.
47. False. 279 items.
48. True.
49. True.
50. True.
51. False. They lack validity.
52. False.
53. False. Symmetrical
54. True.
55. False.
56. True.
57. False.
58. False. In three versions, standard, coloured, and advanced.

59. True.

60. False. This measures 18 traits of normal personality.

61. True.

62. False. It measures three general factors: cognitive factor, perceptual factor and a psychomotor factor.

63. True

64. False. Contains both verbal and performance tests...

65. True. 5 verbal and 5 performance batteries.

66. True.

67. False. It is basically a vocabulary test.

68. False.

69. False. Three forms: The Standard Progressive Matrices, the Coloured Progressive Matrices and the Advanced Progressive Matrices.

70. True.

71. False. It is complex and time-consuming.

72. False. It is quick and easy.

73. True.

74. False. It is low.

75. False. Normal personality.

76. True.

77. False. 16 primary factor scales.

78. False. Only one of the cards is blank for this purpose.

79. True.

80. False. It requires little special training.

81. False. Two human figures.

82. False.

83. False. The stimuli or tasks are ambiguous and are designed to provide a wide range of responses from the subjects.

84. False. It widely used but is relatively unstructured.

85. True.

86. True.

87. False. 10 inkblots.
88. False. The cards contain pictures which provide stimuli for subjects to create stories.
89. False. It is a semi structured projective test.
90. True. It is useful in diagnosing many types of psychopathology including schizophrenia and depression.
91. True.
92. True.
93. True
94. True.
95. False. It tests divided attention.
96. True.
97. True.
98. True. It also has an immediate memory component.
99. True. It has 34 subtests.
100. True. It was developed to assess the personal, interpersonal, and social adjustment psychiatric patients in the community but much of it is also appropriate for the Neuropsychologically impaired individuals.

•————————————•

11. PSYCHOTHERAPIES

1. Transference impedes the work of dynamic psychotherapy.
2. Transference only occurs in the psychoanalytic setting.
3. In psychodynamic psychotherapy it is inappropriate to use humour as a therapeutic tool.
4. Brief focal therapy can be useful for diffused and uncircumcised conflicts.
5. Transference interpretations are not used in brief focal therapy.
6. The concept of enmeshment is associated with Adler.
7. Psychodrama is more suitable for people who are extroverts.
8. Gaining of insight is productive in group therapy.
9. Confabulation is can be regarded as an ego defence mechanism.
10. Ego defence mechanisms distort reality to deal with stressful situations.
11. · Retaliation can be considered as an ego defence mechanism.
12. Feelings experienced by the therapist towards the client are termed as transference.
13. Through transference the client is enabled to deal with negative thoughts.
14. According to Freud, ego contains moral values.
15. According to Freud, the anal stage is at age 3-4.
16. Adler put forward the concept of archetypes.
17. Jung gave the concept of collective unconscious.
18. According to Winnicot the 'depressive position occurs after the paranoid position.'
19. Flooding is a type of systematic desensitization.
20. Flooding is more effective than systematic desensitization.

21. In supportive psychotherapy, analysis of transference may be done.

22. In supportive psychotherapy, behavioural modification may be done.

23. Spectatoring is a term used in family therapy.

24. Rubber fence is a concept used in family therapy.

25. Imprinting is a strategy employed by behavioural therapists.

26. According to Piaget, cognitive child development takes place gradually.

27. Thought blocking is a technique used by behavioural therapists.

28. According to Yalom, leader assertiveness is a therapeutic factor in group psychotherapy.

29. Beck's theory of depression includes the concept of learned helplessness.

30. Modelling is considered to be of limited value in adults.

31. Behavioural psychotherapy based on principles of reciprocal inhibition, has been useful in the treatment of obsessive-compulsive disorders.

32. The concept of transference is at the core of transactional analysis.

33. Behavioural therapy also lays emphasis on the importance of unconscious processes.

34. Freud also made contributions to group psychology.

35. Group therapy derives more from behavioural than a psychoanalytical theoretical approach.

36. In psychoanalytic psychotherapy, the latent content of the dreams should be interpreted.

37. Transference involves feelings of love and hate.

38. The term Treatment Alliance refers to a fundamental precondition of analytic treatment.

39. Counter transference is the interpretation of the transference by the therapist.

40. The term Negative Therapeutic Reaction is used when the patient refuses to start treatment.
41. In Brief psychotherapy the therapists avoids interpreting the transference.
42. According to psychoanalytical theory, the fixation at the anal phase is related in adult life to obstinacy and frugality.
43. The superego usually includes unconscious elements.
44. Circularity and homeostasis are the key theoretical concepts of Systems therapy.
45. Sublimation and displacement are mature defence mechanisms.
46. Gestalt psychology states that the whole is different from the sum of its part.
47. Gestalt psychology emphasizes the current experiences of the patient in here and now.
48. Gestalt psychology states that the properties of some details in a pattern influence how the whole pattern is perceived.
49. Perception, According to Gestalt psychology includes law of infinity.
50. In psychoanalytic theory, fixation at the oral stage is related in adult life to stubbornness.
51. Identification and introjection are immature defence mechanisms of ego.
52. Systemic desensitization involves the construction of a hierarchy of anxiety-provoking stimuli.
53. Systematic desensitization substitutes constructive responses for maladaptive ones.
54. Sculpting is a concept in family therapy.
55. Circular reaction is a concept in family therapy.
56. The behavioural approach focuses on the historical determinants of behaviour.
57. Transactional analysis involves "game analysis".
58. Cathexis is a release of repressed material accompanied by a release of tension.

59. Cathexis is an element of libido theory.

60. Type A can be measured by the Framingham Scale.

61. Type A behaviour has been shown to be correlated with neuroticism.

62. Rogerian Client Centred Therapy emphasizes the use of dereflection.

63. The concepts of anima and shadow are associated with Jung.

64. Primal therapy emphasizes the pain of infantile emotional trauma.

65. According to psychoanalytic theory, regression is the principal underlying defence.

66. According to Munuchin, the concepts of appropriate alliances, boundaries and hierarchies are said to be essential to a healthy functioning family systems.

67. Aversion therapy includes flooding.

68. Implosive therapy involves the patient imagining anxiety-provoking stimuli.

69. Implosive therapy requires anxiety to be experienced without any actual adverse consequences.

70. Operant conditioning is associated with shaping.

71. Bion's name is associated with the "Encounter Group".

72. Systemic desensitization requires modelling.

73. According to Freud, primary process thinking is rational.

74. The basic defence mechanism is regression.

75. Severe borderline personality is a contradiction for Brief dynamic therapy.

76. Transference is seldom interpreted in behaviour therapy.

77. Interpretations in psychoanalytic therapy are most effective when referring to the transference.

78. The concept of projective identification is associated with Melanie Klein.

79. Jung emphasized the role of birth order.

80. Ainsworth devised Strange Situation test to study the effects of separating infants from their mothers.
81. Winnicot described "good enough mother".
82. Munuchin is associated with Systemic Family therapy.
83. Foulkes described "mirror reaction".
84. Systemic desensitization is the appropriate treatment for obsessive compulsive disorder.
85. A graded hierarchy of feared situations is the critical effective component of Systemic desensitization.
86. The technique of Token Economy is based on operant conditioning.
87. According to Freud, primary process thinking includes condensation, displacement and symbolization.
88. Parapraxes are held to be the evidence of preconscious or unconscious thoughts.
89. The basic defence mechanism is repression.
90. Projection is associated with paranoia.
91. Severe OCD is often amenable to psychoanalytic therapy.
92. Defence mechanisms are the function of the ego.
93. In OCD, defences such as isolation, magical undoing and reactive formation operate.
94. Severe borderline personality disorder is a relative contradiction to Brief dynamic therapy.
95. Interpretations in analytic therapy are held to be most effective when referring to transference.
96. The Milan systemic school is associated with circularity, neutrality, and hypothesising.
97. Projective identification is a primitive defence mechanism.
98. Projective identification is a part of the paranoid schizoid position.
99. Transference is characteristic of narcissistic personalities.
100. Classical psychoanalysis views anxiety as a threat from the superego.

101. The paranoid schizoid position reflects ambivalence to the mother.

102. According to Melanie Klein, the depressive position is associated with separation anxiety.

103. According to Melanie Klein, projective identification is compatible with the healthy development of the ego.

104. According to Melanie Klein, the depressive position is linked to reparation.

105. Good ego strength is manifest by long standing relationships.

106. Counter transference is to be fostered during treatment.

107. Counter transference is always counter productive.

108. Mary Main devised a procedure to study the effects of separating infants from their mothers.

109. Ainsworth devised the Adult Attachment Interview.

110. In psychoanalytic terms, depression is a form of introjection.

111. In psychoanalytic terms, schizophrenia is explained by regression.

112. Rationalization is a narcissistic defence mechanism.

113. Reaction formation is a narcissistic defence mechanism.

114. One of the essential requirement of nearly all forms of psychotherapies is to have at least one stable relationship in the past.

115. According to psychoanalytic theory, sublimation is one of the mechanisms involved in dreams.

116. In behavioural psychotherapy response prevention is characteristically combined with flooding.

117. Simple phobias are best treated by relaxation therapy.

118. According to psychoanalysis, transference is a form of conscious resistance.

119. Imprinting is an important concept of behaviour therapy.

120 In psychoanalysis, the term countercathexis is a form of resistance.

121. According to Fairburn, object relationship determines libidinal attitude.

122. In dysfunctional families, myths play a detrimental role.

123. Enmeshment is a positive feature of healthy families.

124. The incidence of homosexuality increases in people who are sexually abused.

125. According to Freud's topographical model, unconscious is time-limited.

126. According to Freud, primary process thinking includes condensation.

127. Kleinian's paranoid-schizoid position includes defence mechanisms of intellectualization, denial and projective identification.

128. Winnicot originated the concept of good-enough mother.

129. Abreaction eliminates the cause of conflict.

130. There is evidence that females undergoing psychotherapy have better outcome as compared to males.

●━━━━━━━●

11. PSYCHOTHERAPIES
ANSWER

1. False.
2. False.
3. False.
4. False.
5. False.
6. False.
7. False.
8. True.
9. False.
10. True.
11. False.
12. False.
13. False.
14. False.
15. False. 2 years.
16. False. Jung.
17. True.
18. False. Melanie Klien.
19. False.
20. True.
21. False.
22. False.
23. False. Used in sexual therapy.
24. True. Imaginary boundary between the family systems.
25. False. A term used in ethnology.
26. False. Suddenly in leaps.
27. False. Thought stopping.

28. False.
29. False. Seligman.
30. True.
31. False.
32. False.
33. False.
34. True.
35. False.
36. True.
37. True.
38. True.
39. False.
40. False.
41. False.
42. True.
43. False.
44. True. Circularity rules appear to govern repetitive sequences of behaviour between couples. Homeostasis is the notion of consistency of interaction.
45. False.
46. True.
47. False.
48. False.
49. False.
50. False. Anal stage
51. True.
52. True.
53. True.
54. True.
55. False.
56. False.

57. True
58. False.
59. True.
60. True.
61. True.
62. False.
63. True.
64. True.
65. False.
66. True
67. False.
68. True.
69. True.
70. True.
71. False.
72. False.
73. False.
74. False.
75. True.
76. True.
77. True.
78. True.
79. False.
80. True.
81. True.
82. False.
83. True.
84. False.
85. False.
86. True
87. True.

Psychotherapies
Answer

88. True.

89. True.

90. True.

91. True.

92. True.

93. True.

94. True.

95. True.

96. True.

97. True.

98. True.

99. False

100. True.

101. True.

102. False.

103. True.

104. True.

105. True.

106. True.

107. False.

108. False.

109. False.

110. True.

111. True.

112. False. Neurotic defence mechanism.

113. False. Neurotic defence mechanism.

114. True

115. False.

116. True.

117. False.

118. False. Unconscious resistance.

119. False. It is a concept by Lorenz
120. True.
121. True.
122. True.
123. False. This means that parents are over-involved with their children and is feature of dysfunctional families.
124. True.
125. False. It is timeless.
126. True.
127. False. Not denial.
128. True.
129. False. It may open the way for further exploration of repressed feelings and experiences.
130. False. There is no evidence to suggest this.

12. RESEARCH METHODOLOGY

1. A nominal scale of measurement is one in which numbers are used to classify and identify persons.
2. Ordinal measurement is rarely used in psychology.
3. The reliability of the test I whether the test adequately measures what it is supposed to measure.
4. In ratio scale the size of the difference between the numbers assigned to two persons or objects corresponds to the degree to which these persons or objects differ on the attribute being measured.
5. Factor analysis is a statistical technique used to analyze patterns of correlation among measures.
6. A valid test is one that yields consistent scores when a person takes two alternate forms of the test or when he or she takes the same test on two or more occasions.
7. A ratio scale of measurement is one in which ratios between the numbers assigned to persons or objects correspond to ratios between the attributes measured in these persons or objects.
8. Nominal scales are the most informative scales.
9. Correlation coefficient measures the statistical relationship between two variables, without assuming that either is dependent or independent.
10. The Likert scale is an equal interval scale.
11. Reliability in measurement includes an alternative forms type.
12. Ratio scales are the most useful and informative scales and are common in psychology.
13. Reliability is the consistency of test scores.
14. The least number of expected values which has to be

calculated before all the others can be deduced is known as the degrees of freedom.

15. Halo effect occurs when researchers alter the situation by their presence.

16. Independent variable is used to measure the affect of the dependent variable.

17. Validity is the measure of extent to which test scores differ or vary.

18. Central limit theorem means that as the sample size increases, the sample mean will approach a normal distribution, no matter what the shape of the parent population is.

19. Multivariate analysis of variance (MANOVA) is a statistical test where three or more groups are compared on a single continuous measure.

20. A confounder is a variable associated with exposure, outcome and casual pathway.

21. Regression to the mean is the tendency for extreme values on a measure to increase with repeated measurement or time.

22. A result which is statistically significant is highly unlikely to have occurred by chance alone.

23. The mean gives no information about the data distribution, whereas the median does.

24. The confidence interval gives the precision of a measure.

25. Percentile rank is a type of norm that describes a score in terms of the percentage of a norm group who achieves that score or a lower one.

26. Generalizability theory   is a theory of measurement that attempts to determine only the sources of consistency in test scores.

27. In nominal data different categories are quantitatively different from each other.

28. The one-sample-t-test can be used to assess the statistical significance of the difference between the mean of a sample

of subjects and a population value.

29. Split-half method of reliability involves two administrations of the same test.

30. Kappa is the measure of agreement between decisions obtained in two separate tests.

31. Categorical or nominal data is where each observation is allocated to one or two 'named' categories.

32. Correlation coefficients range from (-5 to + 5).

33. In continuous data different scores are qualitatively different from each other.

34. Interval and ratio data can be added, subtracted, multiplied or divided.

35. In non-parametric tests the data is normally distributed.

36. Compared with validity, the reliability of a measuring instrument is a much more difficult property to assess.

37. Confidence interval is the range of values in which we can be 90% confident that the true value of a given population parameter lies.

38. Correlation is a measure of the degree of association between two or more variables.

39. The interquartile range is the difference between 25th and 50th percentile scores.

40. Mann-Whitney U Test is the non-parametric equivalent of the two sample t-test.

41. In normal distribution the mean and median are the same but mode is different.

42. Variance is the measure of the dispersion of data about the mean.

43. The two-sample-t-test can be used to assess the statistical significance of the difference between the means of two groups of subjects.

44. Non-parametric test is more powerful than the equivalent parametric test.

45. The mean is the middle value of the scores when the scores are placed in rank order of magnitude.
46. Non-parametric tests can be used with nominal and ordinal data.
47. Parametric test is more appropriate for non-normal or skewed data, small samples or ordinal data.
48. Wilcoxon Signed Rank Sum Test is the non-parametric equivalent of the two samples T-test.
49. Factor analysis segregates data into the maximum number of dimensions that define a group.
50. Non-parametric test tend to give a less significant P-value.
51. Standard error is the number of standard deviations on either side of the mean.
52. Skewness measures deviation from normal distribution curve.
53. Variance is the mean of the sum of squares.
54. Mean deviation is the square root of the variance.
55. In normal distribution, 68.2 % of all scores lie within 1.96 standard deviations from the mean score.
56. Wilcoxon Signed Rank Sum Test is a non-parametric test.
57. Test-retest reliability is established by administering the measure to a group of subjects on two occasions separated by a designated period of time.
58. Criterion validity determines whether a measure discriminates between people who are known to be dissimilar on a feature external to the measure itself.
59. The specificity of the case is defined as the proportion of positive cases correctly identified.
60. Content validity is concerned with weather the instrument adequately probes the specific domain that one requires.
61. The sensitivity of the case is the proportion of negative cases correctly identified.

62. In the context of testing, bias and fairness represent fundamentally different concepts.

63. The use of norms, i.e. an external reference, helps to enhance interpretability of scores.

64. A normative score provides information about an examinee's performance in comparison to the (total) score distribution of some reference group or norm sample representing a well-defined population.

65. Power is defined as the probability of rejecting he null hypothesis when, in the real world, it should have been rejected.

•————————————•

12. RESEARCH METHODOLOGY
ANSWER

1. True
2. False. It is extremely common.
3. False. This is validity of the test.
4. False. This is interval scale.
5. True.
6. False. This is reliability.
7. True.
8. False. These are the least informative.
9. True.
10. True.
11. True.
12. False. Although very useful and informative they are rare in psychology because a meaningful zero point is often difficult to achieve.
13. True.
14. True.
15. False. This is called Hawthorne effect.
16. False. Dependent variable is used to measure the effect of the independent variable.
17. False. This is variance.
18. True.
19. False. This is analysis of variance (ANOVA).
20. False. Not on the casual pathway.
21. False. Values decrease.
22. True.
23. False. Median gives no information, whereas mean does.
24. True.
25. True.

26. False. It looks for both consistency and inconsistency in test scores

27. False. Qualitatively different.

28. True.

29. False. This is Test-retest method. Split-half method of estimating reliability involves comparing performances on half of the test with performance on the other half.

30. True. It is used in assessing the reliability of criterion-referenced tests.

31. True.

32. False. From (-1 to + 1).

33. False. Scores are quantitatively different from each other.

34. True.

35. False.

36. False. Validity is more difficult to assess.

37. False. 95%

38. True.

39. False. This is the difference between 25th and 75th percentile scores.

40. True.

41. False. Mean, median and mode are equal.

42. True.

43. True.

44. False. Parametric test is more powerful.

45. False. This is median. Mean is the sum of the values of the individual scores, divided by the total number of scores.

46. True.

47. False. Non-parametric tests are more appropriate for these situations.

48. False. It is equivalent to the one sample t-test.

49. False. Minimum number of dimensions.

50. True.

51. False. This is Z score. Standard error is an estimate of the discrepancy between sample mean and true population mean.
52. True
53. True.
54. False. This is standard deviation. Mean deviation is the average difference of each score from the mean.
55. False. 95% scores.
56. True.
57. True.
58. True.
59. False. This is sensitivity.
60. True.
61. False. This is sensitivity.
62. True. Bias is a statistical characteristic of the test scores or of the predictions based on those scores. Fairness refers to a value judgement regarding decisions or actions taken as a result of test scores.
63. True.
64. True. It is required to describe the normative sample with respect to demographic characteristics.
65. True.

13. SOCIAL PSYCHOLOGY

1. Fundamental Attribution error is the tendency to make internal attributions over external attribution in explaining the behaviour of others.

2. Eye contact tends to diminish in antagonistic behaviour.

3. A directive management style of leadership encourages initiative.

4. Committees tend to make cautious decisions as compared to individuals.

5. Females are more likely to conform to the group than males.

6. Dissonance is decreased by changing the information available.

7. According to Self-Perception theory, we make judgements about ourselves by using the same inferential processes and making the same kind of errors, which we use for making judgements about others.

8. There is sufficient evidence that dominant and submissive partners make satisfactory marriages.

9. Girls are more suggestible than boys.

10. Differences in level of aggression in boys and girls are greater in older children.

11. Explicit messages are more persuasive than for intelligent listeners.

12. In judging other people's behaviour, we commonly overestimate the role of situational factors.

13. The frustration-aggression hypothesis has little empirical support.

14. The performance of a group increases with a directive leader, irrespective of intellectual ability.

15. The presence of others enhances performance on new tasks.

16. While in groups people feel more responsible for their

decisions and actions.

17. Instrumental aggressions is goal directed and is emotional driven.

18. Conformity continues to increase in a linear relationship with group size.

19. Measured attitudes are reliable predictors of behaviour.

20. There is a poor correlation between the individual measures of attitudes.

21. Likert scale is a zero scale.

22. Thurstone scale is an equally appearing interval scale (change).

23. Cognitive dissonance can be increased by changing attitudes.

24. When there is low arousal, high cognitive dissonance would occur.

25. Regarding aggression, most people are at the extremes of either impulsive or instrumental aggression.

26. Physical attractiveness has a small effect on people's judgements of intelligence or predictions about career success.

27. On additive tasks, groups do better than individuals.

28. Thurstone scale is more sensitive than Likert scale.

29. In semantic differential scale there is a ten point visual analogue scale on which the subject marks his or her response.

30. Likert scale consists of a number of statements and for each the subject marks degree of agreement or disagreement on a seven point scale.

31. Thurstone scale consists of statements which have been ranked and assigned values.

32. Borgadus social distance scale measures racial prejudice.

33. According to Osgood and Tannenbaum's congruity theory, when two attitudes are mutually inconsistent the one that is less firmly held will change.

34. Increased dissonance can occur when the perceived choice is high.
35. Increased dissonance can occur when there is increased pressure to comply.
36. Implicit messages are less persuasive for intelligent people.
37. According to exchange theory of interpersonal attraction, there is preference for relationships that offer greatest gains with least expense.
38. According to attribution theory, individuals tend to attribute their own behaviour to situational factors but that of others to dispositional causes.
39. Bias in attributing our own behaviour to external causes is called the fundamental attribution error.
40. French and Raven described eight types of methods by which people influence other individuals or groups.
41. Lewin described four types of leadership styles.
42. According to Fiedler's contingency theory, high LPC score (least preferred co-worker) person is task orientated.
43. According to Fiedler's contingency theory, low LPC score (least preferred co-worker) person is relationship-orientated.
44. To reduce prejudice there should be more contact with non-stereotypes.
45. According to social learning theory, aggression is considered to be a basic instinct.
46. Affective components in attitudes are very resistant to change.
47. Measured attitudes are good predictors of behaviour.
48. One of the disadvantages of Thurstone scale (attitudes) is that the ranking may be biased.
49. One of the disadvantages of Thurstone scale (attitudes) is that different response patterns may result in the same mean score.
50. Likert scale is a ten point scale indicating the level of agreement with presented statements.

51. Semantic differential scale has low test-retest reliability.

52. Semantic differential scale is a twenty -five point scale indicating level of agreement with presented statements.

53. According to Hieder's balance theory, each individual strives to achieve balance or harmony in the attitudes, perceptions and beliefs.

54. Regarding persuasive communication, high-esteem and intelligence of the recipient increase the likelihood that complex messages will be persuasive.

55. Regarding persuasive communication, being an opinion leader is one of the characteristic of persuasive communicators.

56. Regarding persuasive communication, implicit messages are more persuasive for the less intelligent recipient.

57. Interpersonal attraction is determined in part by proximity, physical attractiveness, similarity, and reciprocity.

58. Regarding Attribution theory, covariation principle suggests that people should attribute behaviour to a casual factor if that factor was present whenever the behaviour occurred but was absent whenever it did not occur.

59. According to Lewin, a democratic leader is good for emergency situations.

60. According to Lewin, workers will abandon task in autocratic leader's absence.

61. According to Lewin, a democratic leader is good for person-orientated tasks.

62. Regarding social facilitation, Distraction-conflict theory suggests that the presence of others enhances the individual's desire to present a favourable image.

63. The fundamental attribution error represents the dual tendency for people to underestimate dispositional factors and to overestimate situational factors when searching for the cause of some behaviour.

64. French and Raven described three types of social power.

65. Situations in which an individual conforms to an opinion in public but sticks to a different view in his own mind are called normative social influence.

66. Regarding conformity, normative influence processes include wanting to be correct and to understand the right way to act in a given situation.

67. According to Cook, equal status is one of the conditions to reduce prejudice.

68. According to social learning theory, aggression is a basic instinct.

69. Altruistic behaviour occurs throughout animal kingdom.

70. Altruistic behaviour can be explained by the concept of inclusive fitness.

71. The principle of inclusive fitness can be applied to the risk of child abuse from step-parents.

72. Xenophobia means hatred of distant relatives.

73. According to Trivers, reciprocal altruism means helping others and expecting help in return.

74. Regarding inclusive fitness, Haldene argued that in small population of related individuals, natural selection would favour the spread of genes controlling certain types of altruistic behaviour.

75. A male olive baboon helping another male defeat a rival despite the risk of injury is an example of reciprocal altruism.

76. Bystander intervention should be less common among smaller anonymous communities than among larger integrated ones.

77. Between strangers, helping is more likely to occur when there is low cost to the donor and has higher benefit for the recipient.

78. The principles of inclusive fitness and reciprocal altruism explain how the helping behaviour could have arisen from the unselfish process of natural selection.

79. The principles of competition and cooperation are central to

the understanding of all social interactions.

80. The evolution bi-parental care is characteristics of many birds, human species and chimpanzees. .

81. Poyandry means that one male mates with many females.

82. Triver's parental investment theory refers to the total amount of money and time spent in rearing their offspring.

83. According to Triver's parental investment theory of sexual selection, where there is no further parental investment, the imbalance in gamete leads to male choice and female competition.

84. Triver's parental investment theory can explain sexual jealousy and marital violence.

85. Studies of mate preferences show that females value status and wealth, whereas men value physical attractiveness and youth.

86. Studies have found physical attractiveness is valued less in areas of the world where there is greater prevalence of pathogens.

87. The term cuckoldry refers to the case of a man bringing up another's child.

88. Game theory explains the sexual behaviour of animals.

89. According to game theory, the evolutionary stable strategy or ESS is the point where the strategy can be replaced by any other.

90. According to game theory, animals make judgements of the likely costs of confronting an opponent before the contest and also do it during the fight.

91. Unidirectional model of socialization means that the impetus for change and regulation from the individual being socialized.

92. The mutuality model of socialization represents the child as an active participant in social development.

93. Research has shown that infants prefer parents who sit still rather than who move and talk.

94. Research show that infants prefer human voices to other sounds.

95. Research shows that infants prefer faces to other symmetrical shapes.

96. Research shows that from the very beginning the infant is passively involved in his or her social development.

97. Attachment behaviour occurs throughout life.

98. According to Dollard and Miller's Secondary Drive hypothesis, caregivers become associated with meetings the primary drives (feeding) and therefore proximity to the caregiver becomes a need (secondary drive).

99. According to Bowlby, attachment process is an adaptive system of behaviour that has evolved to maximize the infant's survival prospects.

100. According to Bowlby, some children become attached to parents who neglect or abuse them.

101. According to Bowlby's attachment theory, behaviours that promote attachment emerge as a result of reinforcement contingencies.

102. According to Bowlby's theory of attachment, attachment behaviours help ensure that the infant develops a secure base.

103. Research show that attachment is a normative development.

104. Studies confirm that attachment occurs in children at different age span in various countries.

105. According to Ainsworth, there are four kinds of attachment relationships.

106. According to Ainsworth, Type A attachment behaviour is securely attached behaviour (Securely attached).

107. According to Ainsworth, 10 percent of infants exhibit Type attachment behaviour (Anxious/avoidant).

108. According to Ainsworth, 10 percent of infants show Type C attachment behaviour (Anxious/ambivalent).

109. Researchers have shown that children with Type B attachment behaviour score high on measures of interpersonal competence and cognitive development during their preschool and kindergarten years.

110. Researchers have shown that children with Type A attachment show higher scores on measures of toy play and exploratory skills during their preschool and kindergarten years.

111. According to attachment theorists, attachment is unidirectional.

112. According to attachment theorists, secure base is fundamental to subsequent development.

113. According to Shaver and colleagues, adult's romantic orientations can be categorized in three main types that are different to Ainsworth's categories of attachment types.

114. Adults also exhibit the three characteristics of secure, anxious/ambivalent and anxious/avoidant attachments.

115. Research has shown that persons with different attachment styles exhibit different styles of religious commitments.

116. Regarding social development, Vygotsky social theory states that a child is like a scientist engaged in dispute with his or her peers.

117. Regarding social development of children, researchers have shown that understanding of society is closely linked to cognitive development.

118. Research has shown that hot temperature produces increases in aggressive motives and tendencies.

119. Implicit personality theories emphasize general beliefs about the frequency and variability of personality traits for individual or groups.

120. Experiments have shown that conformity increases when we are made to feel incompetent or insecure.

121. Regarding conformity, internalisation means that a private belief becomes inconsistent with public belief or opinion.

122. Social judge ability theory focuses on the conditions under which people feel entitled to judge.

123. The Social judge ability theory does not account for the dilution of stereotypes.

124. Attribution theory is not one single body of ideas and research but a collection of numerous theoretical contributions.

125. According to Heider, when we observe others we tend to search for enduring, unchanging, and dispositional characteristics.

126. According to Hieder, we tend to attribute behaviours to events that are present when the e outcome is present and absent when the outcome is absent.

127. According to Hieder, we usually do not distinguish between intentional and unintentional behaviours.

128. According to Hieder, we tend to explain the behaviour in terms of dispositional and situational factors.

129. According to Hieder, correspondent behaviour means that the disposition attributed to a person, corresponds to the behaviour itself.

130. According to Jones and Davis, we tend to make correspondent inferences about other people's behaviour all the time.

131. According to Jones and Davis, a precondition for a correspondent inference is the non -attribution of intentionality.

132. Like Jones and Davis, Easer also argued that intentions are a precondition for correspondent behaviour.

133. According to the co variation model of attribution, if two events repeatedly occur, we are more likely to infer that they are casually related than if they rarely co-occur.

134. According to Kelly, an attribution about some behaviou depends upon the extent to which it co varies with consensus consistency and distinctiveness information.

135. According to Kelly's theory of attribution, consistency reefers to the extent to which other people behave in the same way towards the same stimulus.

136. According to Kelly's theory of attribution, distinctiveness refers to the extent to which a person reacts in the same way towards other stimuli.

137. According to Kelly's theory of attribution, consistency refers to the stability of behaviour, that is, the extent to which a person has reacted in the same way to the same stimulus on other occasions.

138. According to Hilton and Slugoski's theory of attribution, we attribute as a cause the necessary condition that is abnormal when compared with the background of the target event.

139. The fundamental attribution error is also known as correspondence bias.

140. According to discounting principle of attribution, when different causes can produce the same effect, the role of a given cause is discounted if other plausible causes are present.

141. According to the augmenting principle of attribution, the role of a given cause is increased if the effect occurs in the presence of an inhibitory factor.

142. The fundamental attribution error is a failure to use the discounting principle.

143. Regarding attribution, we can, in some situations, overestimate the importance of situational factors as causes for other people's behaviour.

144. Fundamental attribution errors is a universal phenomenon.

145. Regarding fundamental attribution error, the greater the personal relevance an action has the less likely the fundamental attribution error is.

146. The actor-behaviour effect refers to the tendency to make different attributions about behaviour depending on whether we are performing it or observing it.

147. Fundamental attribution error is the tendency for us to take the credit when things turn out to be right and to shun responsibility when they go wrong.

148. Kelly's configuration model tries to account for single event attributions in terms of multiple sufficient and multiple necessary causal schemata.

149. According to Kelly's configuration model of attribution, single event attributions are associated with the augmenting principle.

150. According to Bruner and Tagiuri, our perception of others is based on what others really are rather than our own expectations about them.

151. According to Ash, when people are informed about certain characteristics of another person, people assume that the said person also has certain other characteristics.

152. According to Implicit personality theory, conscious inference processes enable us to form impressions of others.

153. Regarding interpersonal attraction, Rubin has developed two 10-items scales to measure loving and liking.

154. The Dyadic Adjustment Scale is a measure of marital adjustment.

155. Winch's complimentary theory regarding attraction of dissimilarities (e.g. one partner is high on a need such as dominance, while other is low on it), has been generally supported by subsequent research .

156. Deindividuation often occurs when group participation makes people less aroused.

157. Physical attractiveness is unrelated to their self-esteem and happiness.

158. Research has shown that women with more attractive partners have a better sense of humour than women with less attractive partners.

159. Research has shown that women with more attractive

partners are more neurotic than women with less attractive partners.

160. Regarding relationships, interdependence theory distinguishes satisfaction from dependence.

161. Research has consistently shown that as compared with girls, boys have more verbal as well as physical aggression.

162. Research has shown that girls are more suggestible than boys.

163 Research has shown that differences in aggression between boys and girls are smaller in younger children.

164. Self-serving bias leads people to take credit for their achievements while denying their responsibility for their failures.

165. The tendency of people in a group to exert less effort when pooling their efforts towards attaining a common goal than when individually accountable is called social facilitation.

166. Facial expressions are a better indicator of true feelings than bodily cues or tone of voice.

167. Members of a group with a democratic leader abandon the task in the leader's absence.

168. Cognitive dissonance may be reduced by adding new cognitions which are consonant with pre-existing ones.

169. Cognitive dissonance is not usually recognized by the subject.

170. According to attribution theory, in internal attribution, distinctiveness is high, and consensus and consistency are low.

171. The fundamental attribution error means that we tend to over attribute the behaviour of others to external factors.

172. The "contact hypothesis" suggests that we are more likely to reduce our prejudices when we are exposed to members of the other group who are of higher status.

173. Deindividuation may cause people to perform aggressive or illegal acts in certain situations.

174. Regarding conformity, ambiguity of the situation increases the likelihood of conforming to a group norm.

175. Regarding conformity, "social impact theory" holds that the power of a group depends on how important and how close that group is to the person in question.

176. Task orientated leaders are more effective when the task is structured.

177. Person-orientated leaders are most effective when the group is working under time pressure.

178. Likert scale is used to measure attitudes.

179. For intelligent people, explicit messages are more persuasive.

180. If a message is repeated, the chances of it to persuade others increase.

181. Cognitive dissonance is associated with increased arousal.

182. For less intelligent people, two-sided discussions are more convincing.

183. Laissez-faire leadership is beneficial for person-oriented tasks.

184. The pressure for conformity in a group increases if the group is not unanimous.

185. Members of a majority group tend to perceive their own members as more heterogeneous than individuals who are members of a different group.

186. Social loafing occurs when an individual works harder as compared to when he is alone.

187. According to Parkes, multiple bereavements have detrimental effect on self-trust.

188. According to Dans-Moore theory, social stratification is beneficial for society.

189. Research suggests that if one is present in a mixed sex group, the conformity increases.

190. The ultimate attribution error occurs when positive actions by people from other ethnic or social group are attributed to external causes.

191. An attitude consists of 2 components.

192. Regarding social perception, schemas influence what we pay attention to and what we ignore.

193. According to Cognitive Dissonance theory, there is low dissonance when there is awareness of personal responsibility for the consequences of an action.

194. Regarding social perception, schemas can create self-fulfilling prophecies.

195. Heider's Attribution theory states that we explain only other people's behaviour.

196. The fundamental attribution error refers to the tendency to over attribute our behaviour to internal factors.

197. Cognitive dissonance can be reduced by rationalization.

198. One of the advantages of Thurstone scale is that different response patterns may result in the same mean score.

199. Sterotyping rarely leads to prejudice.

200. Contact hypothesis suggests that intergroup contact can slightly increase prejudice.

201. Regarding social influence, norms determine the rules for behaving in a particular situation.

202. During the state of individuation, people may become aggressive or do other illegal things which they do not usually do.

203. Social loafing occurs when some people work harder in a group.

204. There is strong evidence that women conform more than men.

205. According to Rotter's Locus of control theory, external locus is associated with a poor response to stress.

206. The scale of life events is not applicable in underdeveloped countries.

207. Type A behaviour includes competitiveness, impatience and time urgency.

208. According to Seligman's theory of learned helplessness, people become depressed when they feel helpless in bringing about a change in their environment.

209. For measurement of stressful life events, The Schedule of Recent Experiences has a list of 100 classes of events.

210. The Schedule of Recent Experiences (for measurement of stressful life events) has a high reliability.

211. The Life Events and Difficulties Schedule measures adversity in 50 different areas.

212. The Social Readjusting Rating Scale has high sensitivity.

213. According to Buffering Hypothesis of social support, social support has no relationship with mental health in the absence of high levels of stress.

214. According to Vaughan and Leff, High-expressed emotions (when patient is in touch with relatives for more than 35 hours per week) are a better predictor of relapse than non-compliance with medication.

215. Hobbes instinct theory of aggression is consistent with Freud's and Lorenz's views.

216. According to Freud, the purpose of all instincts is to reduce tension to a minimum and then to maintain the

217. Freud has proposed that Eros and Thanatos are two basic human drives directed toward destruction.

218. Lorenz emphasized that human aggression is non-adaptive.

219. There is lot of support for Lorenz's views about human aggression.

220. Unlike Freud, Lorenz asserted that aggression does not occur in response to environmental stimuli, but spontaneously when aggressive energy builds up.

221. The frustration-aggression theory proposes that aggression is always a consequence of frustration the Existence of frustration will always lead to some form of aggression.

222. According to Miller, frustration may make aggression more likely, it is far from being a sufficient cause of aggressive

behaviour.

223. Miller proposed that frustration produces anger rather than aggression.

224. Berkowitz proposed that aggression, like any behaviour, can be reinforced.

225. Berkowitz has put forward cue-arousal theory of aggression.

226. According to Berwokitz, arousal from one source can be transferred to, and energise, some other response.

227. According to Berkowitz, anger and aggression are parallel rather than sequential processes.

228. Bandura has proposed that aggressive behaviours are learned through the reinforcement and imitation of aggressive models.

229. Bandura showed that children can acquire new aggressive responses merely through exposure to a filmed or televised model.

230. Research has shown that television can act as form of vicarious catharsis helps viewers to get their aggressive feelings out of their systems.

•————————•

13. SOCIAL PSYCHOLOGY
ANSWERS

1.   True.
2.   False.
3.   False.
4.   False.
5.   False. Equal.
6.   False.
7.   True.
8.   False.
9.   False. There is not enough evidence.
10. False. More difference in younger children.
11. ˒ False. Works better for less intelligent people.
12. False.
13. False. High empirical support.
14. False.
15. False. Performance is improved on well learnt task.
16. False. Less responsible.
17. False. It is cognition-based.
18. False. It only increases to a certain limit.
19. False.
20. True.
21. False.
22. True.
23. False. Dissonance can be decreased.
24. False. There is high arousal.
25. False.
26. True.

27. False.

28. False.

29. False. Seven point.

30. False. Five point.

31. True.

32. True.

33. True.

34. True.

35. False. When there is decreased pressure.

36. False. More persuasive.

37. True.

38. True.

39. False. Attributing behaviour of other people to internal causes.

40. False. Five: reward, authority, coercion, expertise, and referential.

41. False. Three: autocratic, democratic and laissez-faire.

42. False. Relationship-orientated.

43. False. Task-orientated.

44. True.

45. False. Psychoanalytic theory.

46. True.

47. . False. Poor predictors.

48. True.

49. True.

50. True.

51. False.

52. False. It is Bipolar Visual Analogue Scale.

53. True.

54. True.

55. True.

56. False. Explicit messages.
57. True.
58. True.
59. False. An autocratic leader.
60. True.
61. True.
62. False. This is Self-presentation theory. Distraction conflict theory suggests that the presence of others distracts the person, causing a conflict over how to allocate attention between the others and the task to be performed.
63. False. Other way round.
64. False. Five types: authority, reward, coercive, referent, and expert.
65. True.
66. False. This is informational influence.
67. True.
68. False.
69. True.
70. True. The concept was first explained by Hamilton (1964). This is a wider concept of fitness, when helping relatives is balanced against reproduction.
71. True.
72. False. Hatred of strangers.
73. True.
74. True.
75. True.
76. False. Less common among larger communities.
77. True.
78. False. Selfish process.
79. True.
80. False. Not of chimpanzees.

81. False. One female mates with many males.
82. False. It refers to the time and effort spent in producing food for the egg cells, and all the processes of feeding, incubating and protecting offspring's.
83. False. Male competition and female choice.
84. True.
85. True.
86. False. Valued more.
87. True.
88. False. Fighting behaviour.
89. False. Strategy can be replaced.
90. True.
91. False. Outside the individual.
92. True.
93. False. Vice versa.
94. True.
95. True.
96. False. Actively involved.
97. True.
98. True.
99. True.
100. True.
101. False. They are built in by nature.
102. True.
103. True.
104. False. Attachment occurs in almost all children within roughly the same age span.
105. False. Three types.
106. False. Type A is Anxious/Avoidant.
107. False. 20 percent.
108. True.

109. False. Type A show this.
110. True
111. False. Bi-directional.
112. True.
113. False. Similar to Ainsworth's typology
114. True.
115. True.
116. False. Child is an active apprentice.
117. True.
118. True.
119. True.
120. True.
121. True.
122. False. Private belief becomes consistent. This is called by some psychologists (e.g Mann) true conformity and can be thought of as a conversion to other people's opinion
123. False.
124. True.
125. True.
126. True.
127. False. We do.
128. True.
129. False. This is Jones and Davis's concept.
130. False. We do it sometimes not always.
131. False. Attribution of intentionality.
132. False. Eiser believed that intentions are not a precondition.
133. True.
134. True.
135. False. This is consensus.
136. True.
137. True.

138. True.
139. True.
140. True.
141. True.
142. True.
143. True.
144. False. Occurs in Western societies.
145. False. More likely.
146. True.
147. False. This is called self-serving bias.
148. True.
149. True.
150. False. Based more on our expectations.
151. True.
152. False. Unconscious processes.
153. False. 13-items scale.
154. True.
155. False.
156. False. More aroused.
157. True.
158. True.
159. False. They are less neurotic.
160. True.
161. False.
162. False.
163. False. Older children.
164. True.
165. False. This is social loafing.
166. False.
167. False.
168. True.

169. True.
170. False.
171. False.
172. False.
173. True
174. True.
175. False.
176. False.
177. False.
178. True.
179. False. Implicit messages are more convincing for intelligent people.
180. True.
181. True.
182. False. For high intelligent people, two-sided discussions are more persuasive.
183. True.
184. False. It decreases.
185. True.
186. False. It occurs when an individual works less in a group than when alone.
187. True.
188. True.
189. True.
190. True.
191. False. Three components, cognitive, affective and behavioural.
192. True.
193. False. High dissonance.
194. True.
195. False. Our own behaviour as well.

135

196. False. Other's behaviour.
197. True.
198. False. This is a disadvantage.
199. False. Usually lead to prejudice.
200. False. It decreases prejudice.
201. True.
202. True.
203. False. People make less effort as their contribution performance is not noticed
204. False.
205. True.
206. False.
207. True.
208. True.
209. False. 43.
210. False. Low reliability.
211. False. 38.
212. False.
213. True.
214. True.
215. True
216. False. To ultimately eliminate them.
217. False. Thanatos is a destructive drive whereas Eros is the drive for pleasure.
218. False. He stated that aggression is instinctive and adaptive.
219. False. There is large evidence to dispute his claims.
220. False. Both share the same views.
221. True
222. True
223. False. This view was put forward by Berkowitz.
224. True. For example, a hired assassin kills for money, and

frustration does not play a casual role in an assassin's aggressive behaviour.

225. True

226. False. This is Zillman's excitation transfer theory.

227. True. His Cognitive-neoassociationistic model states this.

228. True

229. True

230. True. There is, however, is no substantial evidence that television is cathartic for everybody.

14. SOCIAL SCIENCES

1. Imprinting is reversible.
2. Imprinting is independent of environmental factors.
3. According to Parson, sick role, the sick person has the option to seek medical help.
4. According to Parson, a sick person is not responsible for his or her condition.
5. Ethology is helpful in understanding the process of attachment and separation anxiety.
6. High integrity is one of the important models forms which observational learning takes place.
7. Interracial contact is the most effective method of reducing racial prejudice.
8. One of the most effective method to reduce racial prejudice is to improve the image of ethnic minorities.
9. Cognitive dissonance is commonly found in schizophrenia.
10. Cognitive dissonance leads to attitude change.
11. Sign-stimulus is a concept in ethology.
12. Fixed action pattern is a concept in ethology.
13. Cognitive dissonance can arise out of conflicting expectations.
14. Cognitive dissonance would increase if the information creating dissonance is dismissed.
15. Durkheim described idealistic suicide.
16. Larger groups create more conformity.
17. Females are more likely to conform to group beliefs.
18. In semantic differential questionnaires it is important to include negative questions to avoid a positional response bias.
19. Some individuals are able to maintain several conflicting

g attitudes at the same time without any discomfort.
20. Social learning theory emphasizes the tendency to conform to social norms.
21. Goldberg and Huxley described five filters and four levels regarding utilization of psychiatric services.
22. According to Goldberg and Huxley, in utilization of psychiatric services, decision to hospitalize occurs at filter 4.
23. According to Goldberg and Huxley, in utilization of psychiatric services, decision to whether specialist help is needed takes place at filter 3.
24. According to Parson, doctors confer the sick role.
25. According to Parson, sick role gives the patient certain rights and also some obligations.
26. According to Parson's a sick role; patient is under obligation to seek necessary help.
27. According to Parson, sick role exempts the person from blame.
28. Parson gave the concept of "illness behaviour".
29. According to Mechanic's illness behaviour, the ways in which given symptoms may be differentially perceived.
30. Mechanic defined "abnormal illness behaviour".
31. Wynne and Singer suggested that abnormal family communication led to schizophrenia.
32. Bateson gave the concept of schizophrenogenic mother.
33. Fromm and Reichmann gave the concept of double bind theory as the causation of schizophrenia.
34. According to Fromm and Reichmann, schizophrenogenic mother is overprotective, warm and hostile.
35. Lidz proposed marital schism/skew.
36. Goffman emphasized the disadvantages of large psychiatric hospitals.
37. According to Goffmman's concept of batch living, staff appears to live in different world to that of the patients they manage.

38. According to Goffman's concept of batch living, in institutions the normal components of life are often absent.
39. Mortification is one of Goffman's concept about institutions.
40. According to Goffman, mortification process includes betrayal funnel and role-stripping.
41. Barton proposed the concept of institutional neurosis.
42. The syndrome of institutional neurosis as proposed by Barton has symptoms like submissive, apathy and diminished self-esteem.
43. Leisure activities are indicators of social class.
44. The type of residences are indicators of social class.
45. Anorexia nervosa is present more in the lower social class.
46. Bipolar Affective Disorder is more likely to be diagnosed in upper social class.
47. Age of the patient affects referral to psychiatric services.
48. According to Mechanic doctors have a social role of legitimizing the illness.
49. High expressed emotions include the notion of double messages.
50. According to Buffering Hypothesis, social support has bearing on mental health only when there are high levels of stress.
51. The Holmes and Rahe Social Readjustment Scale is self-reported questionnaire.
52. The 'Holmes and Rahe Life Event Scale' and 'Holmes and Rahe Social Readjustment Rating Scale' are synonymous.
53. According to Vaughan and Leff, over-protection is associated with relapse.
54. Illness behaviour is a term given to the ways in which given symptoms may be differentially perceived, evaluated and acted upon by different kinds of persons.
55. According to Zola there are three social triggers which together encompass the ways in which symptoms come to be seen as abnormal.

56. According to Zola, sanctioning refers to the pressure by the doctor to pursue treatment.

57. According to Parson, in accepting the sick role the patient gains two benefits but is expected to fulfil four obligations.

58. Durkheim argued that altruistic suicide, which was produced by over-regulation, was relatively rare.

59. Working class men are likely to have more illnesses and to have higher mortality than middle class men.

60. According to Durkheim, altruistic suicide results because of over integration of the individual in the social group.

61. Suicide rates are higher in single, widowed and divorced as compared to married people.

62. The morbidity of women is lower than men.

63. There is about 10% excess mortality in the unemployed.

64. Poverty has a more important role to play in parasuicide than unemployment.

65. Stillbirths and parental mortality is higher in social class V compared with social class I.

66. Primary deviance refers to the change in behaviour that occurs as a consequence of labelling.

67. Women live on an average about ten years longer than men.

68. Working class men are less likely to be unemployed at any point in time compared with middle class men.

69. Labelling refers to the process whereby individual characteristics are identified by others and given a positive label label.

70. The concept of secondary deviance relates to the actual defining of as state or behaviour as 'deviant'.

71. The pressures on the patient to change their behaviour arise from the social meaning and significance of the label the doctor has applied.

72. Secondary deviance arises from society's reaction to the label given to the person.

73. People who do not possess all the attributes of 'normal people' are seen as socially inferior and hence stigmatised.

74. According to Barton, people who have abnormalities are said to be stigmatised.

75. Szasz has asserted that psychiatric illness is a consequence of the labelling of primary deviance.

76. Institutionalization is a form of depersonalisation induced by 'batch living'.

77. Social class plays significant relationship to health and illness.

78. Social class can affect mortality in all age groups.

79. Nottingham Health Profile found that for energy, pain, emotional reactions, sleep and physical morbidity there is a clear class gradient.

80. The major cause of death among men in USA is strokes, while in Japan it is ischaemic heart disease.

81. Studies have found that people who own their houses are likely to have better health than those in rented accommodation.

82. Initially, the British Registrar General classified occupation into eight different groups.

83. There is inconsistent evidence that material circumstances are implicated in the causation of illness.

84. Weber believed that social class tends to pass from generation to generation through social closure and social reproduction.

85. Dialectical materialism is the economic, political and philosophical system of Marx and Engels.

86. The suicide rate of UK is four times as high as that of Spain.

87. Culture cannot be conceptually distinguished from society.

88. According to Darwin, the development of the human species has come about as a result of random process.

89. There is very little support for Darwin's theory of evolution these days.

90. The term socio-biology was invented by Edward Wilson.

91. Most biologists and sociologists are of the view that human beings have 'instincts'.

92. Sociologists frequently utilize the term ethnocentrism.

93. Semiotic analysis can be very useful in comparing one culture with another.

94. Mead's ideas form the main basis of symbolic interactionism and, have a broad impact in sociology.

95. When individuals enters carceral organizations, they may experience resocialization.

96. Goffman originated the concept of ethnomethodology.

97. Deviance may be defined as non-conformity to a given norm, or a set of norms, which are accepted by some people in a community.

98. The term 'white-collar-crime' refers to crime carried out by those in the more affluent sectors of the society.

99. There is a strong evidence that females law-breakers are quite often able to escape coming before the courts because they are able to persuade police or other authorities to see their actions in a particular light.

100. Victimless crimes are activities in which individuals more or less freely engage without directly harming others.

101. Scheff has suggested that schizophrenia can be understood in terms of residual-rule breaking.

102. Thomas Szasz has insisted that the whole concept of mental illness is a myth, justifying persecution in the name of mental health.

103. The term decarceration implies the negative effect of prolonged hospitalization of mental patients.

104. Studies of mother-infant interaction show differences in treatment of boys and girls even when parents believe their reactions to both are the same.

105. Chodorow's theory of gender development explains the struggle of women to become autonomous and independent beings.

106. Gilligan has developed an analysis of gender differences based on the images adult women and men have of themselves and their attainments.

107. Homosexuality exists in all cultures.

108. Plummer has identified three types of homosexuality within modern Western culture.

109. Recent research done in UK on homosexuality does not support Kinsey's figures.

110. According to Kinsey's research, 2 percent of women were exclusively homosexual.

111. Lesbian couples often have children.

112. A considerable number of prostitutes in the UK come from middle class.

113. Goldstein has classified types of prostitution in four categories.

114. The relationship between classes, according to Marx, is an exploitative one.

115. Although in Marx's theory there are two main classes in society, Marx also recognized the existence of transitional classes.

116. Status is objectively given but class depends on people's subjective evaluation of social differences.

117. According to Wright, there are two main dimensions of control over economic resources in modern capitalistic production, and these allow us to identify the major classes which exist.

118. Parkin disagreed with Marx and Weber that ownership of property is the basic foundation of class structure.

119. Processes of exclusion and unsurpation are involved in social closure.

120. Stratification by gender and age is found in all societies.

121. Plurist theory is based on an interpretation of the political system of modern societies which emphasizes the competitive nature of group interests.

122. Polyandry is fairly common in societies.

123. Marx, Durkheim and Weber believed that religion is in a fundamental sense an illusion.

124. The average British citizen sees a GP about four times a year.

125. Coontz and Handerson have augued that most early societies began with equality between the Sexes.

14. SOCIAL SCIENCES
ANSWERS

1.   False.
2.   False.
3.   False.
4.   True.
5.   True.
6.   False.
7.   True.
8.   False.
9.   False.
10.   True.
11.   True.
12.   True.
13.   True.
14.   False.
15.   False.
16.   False.
17.   False.
18.   True.
19.   False.
20.   False.
21.   False. Five levels and four filters.
22.   True.
23.   True.
24.   True.
25.   True.
26.   True.
27.   True.
28.   False. Mechanic defined this.
29.   True.
30.   False. Pilowsky.

31. True.
32. False. Fromm-Reichmann.
33. False. Bateson.
34. False. Not warm. Rejecting, indifferent and distant.
35. True.
36. True.
37. False. This is binary living and binary management.
38. True.
39. True.
40. True.
41. True.
42. True.
43. True
44. True.
45. False. Upper social class.
46. True.
47. True.
48. True.
49. False.
50. True.
51. True
52. True.
53. True
54. True

55. False. Five social triggers: perceived interference with vocational or physical activity, perceived interference with social or personal relations, the occurrence of interpersonal crises, and a kind of temporalizing of symptomatology and sanctioning.
56. False. It is pressure by the relatives and friends to visit the doctor.
57. False. Two benefits (the patient is temporarily excused his or her normal role and the patient is not responsible for his or her illness) and two obligations (the patient must want to get well, and the patient must cooperate with technically competent help)

58   False. This is fatalistic suicide.

59.   True.

60.   True.

61.   True.

62.   False. It is higher than men.

63.   False. It is higher, about 20-30%.

64.   True.

65.   True.

66.   False. This is secondary deviance.

67.   False. About five years longer than men.

68.   False. More likely to be unemployed.

69.   False. Negative label.

70.   False. This is primary deviance.

71.   True.

72.   True

73.   True

74.   False. Goffman stated this

75.   True.

76.   True. In large hospitals people are processed in groups and they gradually lose their individual autonomy.

77.   True

78.   True.

79.   True. Those lower on the social class scale have worst health

80.   The other way round.

81.   True, at least as measured by mortality.

82.   True. The Registrar General later reduced classification to five groups.

83.   False. The evidence is consistent and strong.

84.   True

85.   True. They were influenced by the Idealism of the German philosopher, Hegel.

86.   True

87.   False. They are, however, very closely connected.

88.   True

89.   False. Although his theory has been refined, Darwin's account are still widely accepted.

90. True. It refers to the applications of biological principles in explaining the social activities of all social animals.
91. False. Most of them agree that human beings do not have any instincts. This is in contrast to what ordinary people believe. As understood in biology and sociology, an instinct is a complex pattern of behaviour that is genetically determined.
92. False. They try to avoid this as far as possible. Ethnocentrism is judging other cultures by comparison with one's own.
93. True. This is non-verbal cultural meanings.
94. True. He was primarily a philosopher. Symbolic interactionism emphasizes the active, creative individual . Mead claims that a key element in our individuality is the symbol. A symbol is something which stands for something else.
95. True. Examples of carceral organizations are mental hospital and prisons etc. Previous accepted values and patterns of behaviour may be disrupted and followed by the adoption of radically different ones.
96. False. It was Garfinkel's idea. It is the study of 'ethnomethods' the folk or lay methodspeople use to make sense of what others do, and particularly what they say.
97. False. By significant number of people
98. True. The term was first introduced by Sutherland.
99. False. There is some evidence.
100. True. The term, however, is not entirely accurate.
101. True. Residual norms are deeply buried rules structuring everyday life.
102. True
103. False.This is the return of large number of people into the community.
104. True
105. False. One of the main criticisms of his theory is that it does not explain this.
106. True
107. True
108. False. Four types; casual homosexuality, situated

homosexuality, personalized homosexuality and homosexuality as a way of life.

109. False. Research tends to support Kinsey's figures.
110. True.
111. True. Some are through a relationship with a man, others through artificial insemination.
112. True
113. False. Two categories, occupational commitment and occupational context. Commitment refers to the frequency with which a woman is involved in prostitution. Context means the type of work environment and interaction process in which a woman is involved.
114. True
115. True.
116. False. It's the other way round. Classes derive from the economic factors associated with property and earnings; status is governed by the varying styles of life groups follow.
117. False.Wright was influenced by Marx and Weber. He identified three dimensions; control over investments or money capital, control over the physical means of production, and control over labour power.
118. False. He agreed with this but insisted that this is only one form of social closure.
119. True. Exclusion refers to strategies that groups adopt to separate outsiders from themselves. Unsurpation refers to the attempts of the less privileged to acquire resources previously monopolized by others.
120. True.
121. True.
122. False. This is when a woman has two or more husbands simultaneously. This is very rare
123. True.
124. True.
125. True.

REFERENCES

Atkinson, l. R., Atkinson, C. R., and Hilgard, R. E. (1983). Introduction to psychology, 8th Edition. New York: Harcourt Brace Jovanovich International.

Atkinson, R., Atkinson, R.C., Smith, E. E., Bem, D. J., and Hoeksema, S.N. (1996). Hilgard's introduction to psychology. USA: Harcourt Brace College.

Buckley, P., Bird, J., and Harrison, G. (1995). Examination notes in psychiatry. A postgraduate text.UK: Butterworth-Heinemann.

Coleman, A.M. (2001). Oxford dictionary of psychology. USA: Oxford University Press.

Curran, S., and Willams, C. J. (1999). Clinical research in psychiatry. A practical guide. UK: Butterworth-Heinemann.

Eysenk, M., and Wesley, A. (1998). Psychology. An integrated approach. USA: Longman Ltd.

Freeman, C., and Tyrer, P. (1992). Research methods in psychiatry, 2nd Edition. UK: The Royal College of Psychiatrists.

Garfield, l. S., and Bergin, E. A. (1986). Handbook of psychotherapy and behaviour change. New York: John Willey & Sons. Giddens, A. (1993). Sociology.UK: Blackwell Publishers Ltd.

Gross, R. (2001). The science of mind and behaviour, 4th Edition. London: Hodder & Stoughton.

Gross, R., and Mcllveen, R. (1998). Psychology. A new introduction. UK: Hodder & Stoughton.

Halligan, W. P., Kischka, U., and Marshall, C. J. (2003). Handbook of clinical psychology. Oxford: Oxford University Press.

Hewstone, E. M., Stroebe, W., and Stephenson, G. M. (1996). Introduction to social psychology, 2nd Edition. UK: Blackwell Publishers.

Holmes, E. J. (1991).Textbook of psychotherapy in psychiatric practice. UK: Churchill Livingstone.

Huffman, K., Vernoy, M., and Vernoy, J. (1997). Psychology in action, 4th Edition. New York: John Wiley &Sons Inc.

Kaplan, H. I, and Sadock, B. J. (2005) Comprehensive textbook of psychiatry, 8th Edition. Baltimore: Williams and Wilkins.

Lezak, D.M. (1995). Neurological assessment, 3rd Edition. Oxford: Oxford University Press.

Lishman, W.A. (1995). Organic psychiatry, 3rd Edition. The psychological consequences of cerebral disorder. UK: Blackwell Science.

Malim, T., and Birch, A. (1998).Introductory psychology.UK: McMillan Press Ltd.
Maxwell, A. E. (1978). Basic statistics for medical and social science students. London: Chapman & Hall.

Mayer, D.G. (1998). Psychology, 5th Edition. USA: Worth Publishers.

Murray, K. R., and Davidshofer, C.O. (2001). Psychological testing. Principles and applications, 5th Edition. USA: Prentice Hall.

Schwartz, H. J., Bleiberg, E., and Weisman, S. H. (1995).Psychodynamic concepts in general psychiatry. Washington: American Psychiatric Press.

Weller, M., and Eyseneck, M. (1992). The scientific basis of psychiatry, 2nd Edition. London: W.B.Saunders Company Ltd.

Weston, D. (1966). Psychology. Mind, brain & culture. USA: John Wiley & Sons.

Woolfe, R., Dryden, W., and Strawbridge, S. (2003). Counselling psychology. London: Sage Publications.

Zimbardo, P.G., and Gerrig, R.J. (1999). Psychology and life, 5th Edition. USA: Longman.